METHUEN'S MONOGRAPHS
ON PHYSICAL SUBJECTS

General Editor: B. L. WORSNOP, B.SC., PH.D.

# LOW TEMPERATURE PHYSICS

# Low Temperature Physics

===

## L. C. JACKSON

*M.Sc. (Lond.); Doc.Wis.Nat. (Leiden); F.Inst.P.*
*Royal Military College of Canada*

LONDON: METHUEN & CO LTD

NEW YORK: JOHN WILEY & SONS INC

*First published in November* 1934
*Second edition, revised, February* 1948
*Third edition, November* 1950
*Fourth edition, revised and reset, November* 1955
*Fifth edition, revised and reset, April* 1962
© 1962 *by L. C. Jackson*
*Printed in Great Britain by*
*Spottiswoode, Ballantyne & Co Ltd*
*London & Colchester*
*Catalogue No. (Methuen)* 2/4019/11
5·1

To A.T.T. and M.B.

# Contents

# Preface to Fifth Edition

Physical investigations at low temperatures continue to be performed at an ever-increasing rate. Since the appearance of the fourth edition of this book much progress has been made in our knowledge of the mechanism of electrical conduction in metals and of the shape of the Fermi surface. We have now a reasonably satisfactory understanding of superconductivity.

Much progress has recently been made in the interpretation of the contrasting properties of liquid helium four and liquid helium three.

A thorough revision of the contents of this monograph was required. The plan of the previous editions has been retained but much of the book has been completely rewritten to bring it up to date.

L. C. JACKSON

*Royal Military College of Canada*
*Kingston, Ontario*
*February 1961*

## CHAPTER I

# The Production of Low Temperatures

## The Liquefaction of Air, Hydrogen and Helium

All physical experiments at very low temperatures involve the use of liquefied (or solidified) gases in some way or other. The liquefaction of gases is thus an important branch of low temperature physics, and the principles underlying the method employed will therefore be discussed briefly, with special reference to the cases of air, hydrogen and helium. With the aid of these three liquefied gases it is possible directly or indirectly to experiment over the whole range from room temperature down to about $0.8°$ K. With the aid of the rarer isotope of helium, $He^3$, a liquid bath with a temperature of $0.3°$ K. can be provided. To obtain still lower temperatures some other method, such as adiabatic demagnetization, described later, must be used.

There are two main types of method available for the large-scale liquefaction of air (and hydrogen and helium), that which employs the Joule-Thomson effect (expansion of a gas with the performance of 'internal' work) to produce the necessary cooling (Linde, Hampson) and that which employs, in part at least, the reversible expansion of the gas with the performance of 'external' work (Claude, Heylandt).

### 'Internal Work' Methods of Gas Liquefaction

The essentials of a liquefier using the Joule-Thomson effect are shown diagrammatically in Fig. 1. Compressed gas enters the inner tube of the 'heat interchanger' H at a pressure $p_A$ and temperature $T_A$. It then expands at the valve V to a pressure $p_B$ and the temperature falls on account of the performance by the gas of 'internal work' in expanding against the forces of attraction between the molecules. The cooled expanded gas then passes up the outer tube of the interchanger, cooling the incoming compressed gas as it does so. The expanded gas leaves the liquefier at the pressure $p_B$ and temperature $T_B$ ($T_B$ is nearly equal to $T_A$ if the interchanger is efficient). The cooler compressed gas expands at V and is thereby further cooled and so on until the temperature at the lower end of the interchanger has fallen by this 'regenera-

1

tive' process sufficiently low for the gas to liquefy. A part of the expanded gas will then liquefy and collect at C (temperature $T_C$).

In such an expansion, provided there is no appreciable change in kinetic energy of the gas or after any change of kinetic energy has subsided, the 'enthalpy' $H$ of the gas before and after expansion remains constant since the process takes place adiabatically, no heat being allowed to enter the system from outside. We therefore have†

$$H_A = U_A + p_A v_A = H_B = U_B + p_B v_B \qquad (1)$$

($U$ = internal energy, $p$ = pressure, $v$ = volume per unit mass.)

Theory indicates that the change of temperature $dT$ which results when the pressure of a gas changes by an amount $dp$ on passing a throttle or expansion valve is given by

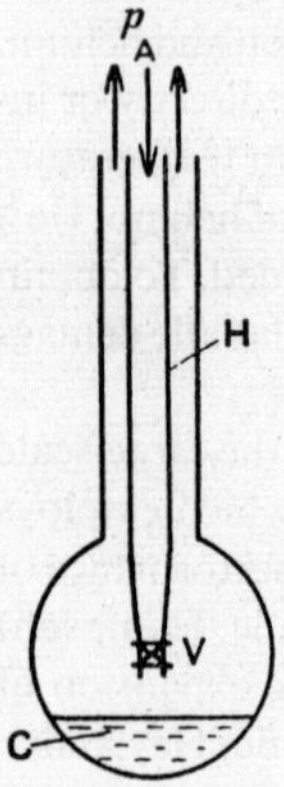

$$\frac{dT}{dp} = \frac{1}{C_p}\left[T\left(\frac{\partial v}{\partial T}\right)_p - v\right] = \frac{T^2}{C_p}\frac{\partial}{\partial T}\left(\frac{v}{T}\right)$$

$$= -\frac{1}{C_p}\left(\frac{\partial H}{\partial p}\right)_T \qquad (2)$$

($C_p$ = specific heat of gas at constant pressure.)

The change of temperature $dT$ is known as the 'differential Joule-Thomson effect', and as appears from (2) its sign depends on the sign of

$$(T(\partial v/\partial T)_p - v)$$

FIG. 1

There is thus a fall in temperature on expansion when this quantity is positive and a rise when it is negative, while there will be no change in the temperature on expansion when $(\partial v/\partial T)_p = v/T$. Points satisfying this condition lie on what is known as the 'inversion curve' and when plotted on a p.t. (reduced pressure and temperature) diagram are found to give a parabola or some similar curve according to the equation of state adopted. Points lying inside the curve represent conditions which lead to cooling on expansion, points outside the curve to warming on expansion.

† For the thermodynamical theory of the Joule-Thomson effect and its 'inversion', see Porter, *Thermodynamics*, Methuen's Monographs on Physical Subjects.

In any actual liquefier the pressure drop is finite and usually large (150 to 1 atm.) and the drop in temperature $\Delta T$ is produced by the 'integral Joule-Thomson effect':

$$\Delta T = \int\limits_{p_A}^{p_B} \frac{T^2}{C_p} \frac{\partial}{\partial T}\left(\frac{v}{T}\right).dp$$

The 'integral effect' also inverts for certain conditions of $p$ and $T$ and gives an 'inversion curve' similar to that of the 'differential effect'.

In applying the Joule-Thomson effect to the liquefaction of gases it is first necessary so to choose the initial pressure and temperature of the gas that expansion produces a fall in temperature throughout the range of temperature which will exist in the liquefier. This condition presents no difficulty with air as the effect is negative at room temperature for any pressure likely to be employed. On the other hand, the effect is positive at room temperature with hydrogen and helium. In actual practice these gases are cooled to 65–90° K. and 15° K. respectively before expansion in order to bring them well inside the 'inversion curve'.

The temperature at which the gas enters the actual liquefier having then been fixed, we can enquire what pressure of the gas before expansion will give a maximum yield of liquid. This can be calculated as follows:

Suppose the liquefier has reached a steady state and is liquefying gas at a constant rate. A certain quantity of gas enters the apparatus per second at a pressure $p_A$ and temperature $T_A$. The gas expands to pressure $p_B$ and a certain fraction $\epsilon$ is liquefied and collects at the bottom of the liquefier at temperature $T_C$. The remainder passes through the heat interchanger and leaves at a pressure $p_B$ and temperature $T_B$. If the interchanger is perfect, $T_B = T_A$. When the steady state has been reached we can equate the enthalpy of the compressed gas entering the liquefier to the sum of the enthalpy of the liquid produced and that of the expanded gas leaving the apparatus. Or, if $H_A$, $H_B$, $H_C$ are the enthalpies per unit mass, we have

$$H_A = (1-\epsilon)H_B + \epsilon H_C$$

$$\epsilon = \frac{H_B - H_A}{H_B - H_C} \tag{3}$$

The fraction $\epsilon$ is known as the efficiency of the liquefier. We have to determine the conditions for which $\epsilon$ is a maximum. Since now $p_B$, $T_B$, $p_C$, $T_C$ and $T_A$ are all fixed by the design of the liquefier, the yield can be varied only by varying $p_A$, the input pressure. From the above formula $\epsilon$ will be a maximum when $H_A$ is a minimum ($H_B$ and $H_C$ are constant).

This occurs when $(\partial H_A / \partial p)_T = 0$. Now from equation (2) the change in temperature produced by the differential Joule-Thomson effect is given by

$$dT = -\frac{1}{C_p}\left(\frac{\partial H}{\partial p}\right)_T . dp$$

Hence the above condition for a maximum yield of liquid requires that the input pressure and temperature are situated on the inversion curve of the differential Joule-Thomson effect. A knowledge of the inversion curve therefore permits the calculation of the most favourable input pressure for any chosen input temperature and the theoretical efficiency can be deduced when $H$ is known as a function of $p$ and $T$.

Thus for air Hausen's data for the Joule-Thomson effect show that the maximum efficiency is obtained when the input pressure is 275 atm. if the air enters at room temperature (290° K.) and expands to 1 atm. pressure. This may be compared with the conditions employed in the Hampson† liquefier, input pressure 150–200 atm., input temperature 290° K., expansion to 1 atm. The theoretical efficiency for these input conditions is such that about 8 per cent of the air entering the liquefier should be drawn off as liquid. This model does not work under the theoretically most favourable conditions but, as it has the advantages of simplicity and ease of manipulation, it was formerly much used for the small-scale production of liquid air for laboratory purposes.

In the larger air liquefiers using the Linde process the overall efficiency is increased by two differences in technique compared with the Hampson process. The air enters the liquefier at 200 atm. pressure after being cooled to about 233° K. by means of an ammonia refriger-

† It is assumed that the reader is familiar with the constructional details of the Hampson and Linde air liquefiers. Diagrams illustrating the processes are to be found in most advanced textbooks on Heat.

ating machine, whereby the fraction of air liquefied is considerably increased. Further, the air expands to about 40 atm. instead of to 1 atm., whereby the Joule-Thomson cooling is not greatly reduced but the amount of work which has to be done in compressing the air is much less. The main bulk of the air has only to be compressed from 40 to 200 atm., and only that fraction of the air which actually liquefies and so leaves the circulation has to be compressed from 1 to 200 atm. Since the work done in compressing a gas isothermally from pressure $p_1$ to pressure $p_2$ is $RT \log (p_2/p_1)$, it will be seen that there is a considerable saving in power required by adopting Linde's procedure. Thus 2·7 kWh. are theoretically required to produce 1 kg. of liquid air by simple expansion from 290° K. and 200 to 1 atm., while only 0·9 kWh. are required if the air is pre-cooled and expanded as in the Linde process. The theoretically most favourable input pressure for an input temperature of 233° K., and expansion to about 40 atm., is 210 atm., in agreement with the figure (200 atm.) actually used.

Similarly one can calculate that the optimum input pressure for the liquefaction of hydrogen is about 160 atm. when the input temperature is between 63° K. and 80° K. and the gas expands to 1 atm. Actually, pressures from 150 to 165 atm. are found to give the greatest yield of liquid, and the efficiency obtained is very close to that calculated theoretically (0·285 in place of 0·295 for the Leiden liquefier with $p_A = 150$ atm., $T_A = 63°$ K.; Keesom, 1928). For helium the optimum input pressure is about 30 atm., for an input temperature of 14° K. and expansion to 1 atm., the calculated efficiency being 0·22. Actually pressures in the range 20–30 atm. are used and efficiencies ranging from 0·13 to 0·19 have been obtained.

The problem of the liquefaction of hydrogen is more complicated than that of air. The compressed gas has to be cooled as far as is readily possible below the inversion temperature before being allowed to expand, some means has to be adopted to prevent the narrow tubes of the liquefier being blocked by the freezing of the traces of impurity present in commercial hydrogen (mainly oxygen) and special precautions have to be taken to eliminate the risk of fire or explosion (a 5 per cent hydrogen–air mixture is violently explosive).

The liquefaction of hydrogen was first achieved by Dewar in 1898. Since that date, many hydrogen liquefiers have been constructed in University, Government and Industrial laboratories throughout the world.† The output of these plants falls mainly within the range of 1–10 litres of liquid per hour, but a few larger ones have been described, one of the largest being that at the Cryogenic Engineering Laboratory, Boulder, Colorado, U.S.A., with an output of 320 litres of liquid hydrogen per hour. With the commercial advent of the Collins helium liquefier, relatively few new hydrogen liquefiers were constructed in the decade following the Second World War and relatively little work was carried out, in the range of temperature obtainable with liquid hydrogen. However, as liquid hydrogen is now in demand for hydrogen bubble chambers used in nuclear physics and as a fuel for guided missiles, very large amounts of the liquid may be produced in the future.

The liquefaction of helium is a matter of still greater difficulty than that of hydrogen as the gas must be cooled to hydrogen temperatures or lower‡ before the Joule-Thomson effect can be used to lower the temperature below the critical temperature $5 \cdot 2°$ K. The elimination of impurities from the helium is still more important and is usually carried out by passing the compressed helium through charcoal cooled with liquid air. Helium was first liquefied by Kamerlingh Onnes at Leiden in 1908 and until 1923 this was the only place in the world at which physical measurements could be made in the range of temperature $1 \cdot 0–4 \cdot 2°$ K. With the spread of interest in low temperature physics many Joule-Thomson helium liquefiers have been described, all employing liquid hydrogen as the cooling agent and only differing in whether or not the incoming high pressure helium is first cooled by (1) heat interchange with the expanded helium gas before being cooled with liquid hydrogen, (2) heat interchange with the vapour from the liquid hydrogen bath, or (3) a liquid nitrogen bath.

*The 'External Work' Methods of Gas Liquefaction*

Suppose a volume of gas $v_1$ enters the cylinder of an engine at a pressure $p_1$ and then expands adiabatically and reversibly, forcing down the piston (supposed frictionless) and doing work on some external system until the volume has increased to $v_2$ and the pressure has fallen

† Descriptions of many of these liquefiers will be found in the works quoted on p. 155, Bibliography, Chapter I.

‡ It is convenient to speak of 'helium' or 'hydrogen' temperatures when referring to the temperatures obtainable with these liquefied gases.

to $p_2$. The outlet valve then opens and the piston rises, forcing the gas out at pressure $p_2$. Then the total amount of work done by the gas will be

$$\int_{p_2}^{p_1} v\,dp = H_1 - H_2$$

and the temperature of the gas will fall from $T_1$ to $T_2$. If the equation of state of the gas can be written as $pv = (C_p - C_v)T$, ($C_p$, $C_v$ specific heat at constant pressure and volume respectively), the work done will be

$$W = C_p(T_1 - T_2) = H_1 - H_2$$

and the final temperature will be given by

$$T_2 = T_1 \left(\frac{p_2}{p_1}\right)^{(C_p - C_v)/C_p} \tag{4}$$

The drop in temperature calculated from (4) is greater than that obtained by throttle expansion from pressure $p_1$ to pressure $p_2$. It would thus seem that it is preferable to cool the gas by the performance of 'external' work rather than 'internal' work in the liquefaction of gases. In actual practice, the difficulties of the realization of the 'external' work method make the two types of process of practically equal efficiency for air liquefaction.

The application of the expansion engine to the liquefaction of gases forms the basis of the Claude and Heylandt methods. Fig. 2 illustrates one of the types of liquefier employing the Claude process. Air compressed to about 40 atm. passes through the interchanger I where it is cooled to about 193° K. by the expanded gas. It then divides, a fraction $M$ passing through the interchanger II and $1 - M$ through the expansion engine E. The gas expands in the engine to 1 atm. pressure (in some Claude liquefiers in two stages, 40–6·3 atm. and 6·3–1 atm.) doing external work, such as driving a dynamo, and is cooled thereby. The cold gas then passes through the interchanger II and cools the fraction $M$ of the high pressure gas. The degree of expansion is so chosen that the temperature of interchangers II and III is considerably lower than the critical temperature of the gas but not as low as its normal boiling point. The fraction $M$ still at the high pressure then condenses in interchangers II and III and after expansion to 1 atm.

collects at L. A portion of the liquid evaporates in the expansion through the valve V and the vapour produced returns to the compressor via the heat interchangers.

The efficiency of the liquefier depends in a rather complicated way on the temperature and pressure of the air before expansion in the engine and the fraction $1 - M$ of the air passing through the engine. For each initial pressure there is a most favourable value of the temperature of the air before expansion in E for every value of $M$, and the actual conditions are best determined by experiment.

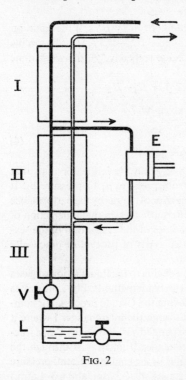

Fig. 2

Typical figures are:

Pressure $= 40$ atm., $M = 0.2$

(i.e. 20 per cent of the air goes through V and 80 per cent through the expansion engine) and $T_2 = 193°$ K.

The Heylandt process differs from the Claude process in detail rather than in principle. In this case the air is compressed to 200 atm. and a fraction $1 - M$ enters the expansion engine at room temperature, interchanger I of Fig. 2 being omitted. After expansion the cold air passes through an interchanger, cooling the fraction $M$ of the compressed air which is then allowed to expand to 1 atm. at a valve and partially liquefies. The temperature of the air leaving the Heylandt expansion engine is above the critical temperature and further cooling of the incoming gas is obtained by the Joule-Thomson effect acting regeneratively.

One of the principal technical difficulties in the application of the external work method is that of maintaining the piston of the expansion engine gas-tight and lubricated in spite of the low temperature of the expanded air. The cylinder of the Claude engine is heat insulated, and so reaches a temperature approximating to that of the expanded air, and the piston is maintained gas-tight by means of a patented impregnated leather cup which needs no further lubrication. The Heylandt engine is not insulated and remains approximately at room temperature so that ordinary lubrication can be employed. It is, however, run at high speed so that the expanded air is swept out of the cylinder before it can cool the latter appreciably.

The Claude process using a pressure of 40 atm. and with a partition ratio $M = 0.2$ requires $0.87$ kWh. per kg. of liquid air produced, thus nearly the same as the Linde process. The Heylandt process using a pressure of 200 atm. and $M = 0.4$ requires about $0.7$ kWh. per kg. of liquid air.†

It has long been realized that an expansion turbine should possess several advantages over the reciprocating engine for the production of low temperatures. It is, however, only in recent years that success has been achieved in designing such a turbine. In 1939 Kapitza produced an air liquefier, working on the Claude principle, which employs an expansion turbine in which the air is expanded from $5.6$ to $1.5$ atm. and operates with an actual overall power consumption of $1.2$ kWh. per kg. of liquid air. The rotor of the turbine, which has a diameter of only 8 cm., revolves at 40,000 rev. per min. and passes $10 m^3$ of air per min., resulting in the production of 20–30 kg. of liquid per hour. Expansion turbines are also used in the Linde-Frenkl plant for the production of oxygen-enriched air and in various other plants for the low temperature separation of gases. The turbine has not been used for the production of liquid hydrogen or liquid helium mainly because it is, in spite of its small size, specially suitable for very large-scale plants.

A laboratory air liquefier of considerable interest, capable of producing 5 litres of liquid air per hour has been developed in recent years by Köhler and Jonkers. In this system air at atmospheric pressure

---

† The power consumptions given above and on p. 5 are theoretical estimates based on the assumption of ideal processes, i.e. strictly isothermal compression in the compressor, no friction losses, no loss of cold, etc. These estimates have to be multiplied by a factor of about 2 to obtain the actual overall power requirements in practice.

condenses on a surface maintained at a temperature of about $-194°$ C. The low temperature is obtained by means of an expansion engine working on a modification of the old Stirling cycle (two constant temperature and two constant volume stages) together with a very efficient heat interchanger of the regenerator type. The working substance in the engine is hydrogen or helium gas and circulates in a closed system. The plant can be run unattended for considerable periods and the absence of any air compressor makes it very convenient for laboratory use.

The first helium liquefier employing the Heylandt principle was designed by Kapitza in 1934 and supplied liquid helium to the Mond laboratory, Cambridge, England, until 1950. Helium at a pressure of 30 atm. is cooled to 65–70° K. with liquid nitrogen, passes through a heat interchanger, expands to 2·2 atm. in an expansion engine and leaves the liquefier via the heat interchangers. A further amount of helium at 15–18 atm. is cooled by the gas from the expansion engine and then expands at a valve, where part of it liquefies. The temperature of the inlet to the engine is 19° K. and that of the outlet 9° K. The final temperature drop to 4·2° K. is obtained by the Joule-Thomson effect at the valve. Ninety-two per cent of the helium passes through the engine and 8 per cent through the expansion valve. Fifty per cent of the latter liquefies and the plant yields 1·7–2·0 litres of liquid helium per hour. As no liquid lubricant can be used at these temperatures, the problem was solved very ingeniously as follows: a gap of 0·05 mm. was left between the cylinder and the piston and a series of shallow grooves was cut in the latter. A small proportion of the compressed helium escapes past the piston and acts as the lubricant, the presence of the grooves reducing the leak and ensuring that the piston moves co-axially with the cylinder.

A major improvement in this type of helium liquefier was made by Collins (1947). In his liquefier helium gas initially at 15 atm. and room temperature is cooled by an expansion engine to 78° K., then by a second expansion engine to 10° K. and finally by a Joule-Thomson expansion to 4·2° K. Liquid helium can be produced by this liquefier at a rate of 2 litres per hour without the use of any other refrigerant or at 4 litres per hour if liquid nitrogen is used to cool the shield around the lower temperature parts of the liquefier. It has later been found possible by doubling the helium gas input and suitably changing the valve settings to produce 8 or more litres of liquid helium per hour. In this liquefier a more efficient heat interchanger is used, the clearance between cylinder and piston is reduced to 0·01 mm., the valve and piston rods are always under tension and so can be made of thin material, the engines and heat interchangers do not have vacuum insulation and the constituent parts are readily accessible for servicing. By making these vital improvements, Collins has transformed the earlier liquefiers into a compact and reliable piece of engineering and, largely as a result of his work, helium liquefaction has become almost a commonplace. The complete liquefier system has been put on the market by A. D. Little, Inc., of Cambridge, Mass., and has become a familiar feature of low temperature laboratories throughout the world.

A further method for the liquefaction of helium which was for a number of years much in use for the small-scale production of liquid helium is the single expansion method developed by Simon. It is, in principle, the simplest method available. Helium gas is compressed into a metal container to a pressure of, say, 150 atm. and is at the same time cooled to 10–11° K. by means of solid hydrogen. The container is then insulated by evacuating the surrounding vessel and the helium allowed to expand slowly, adiabatically and reversibly into a gas-holder until the pressure falls to one atmosphere and part of the gas liquefies. Under these conditions the liquid occupies about 80 per cent of the internal volume of the container. There are two reasons for the very large yield: (i) the thermal capacity of the container is very small compared with that of the compressed helium at these temperatures, (ii) the density of helium gas at 150 atm. and 11° K. is about 50 per cent greater than the density of liquid helium at 1 atm. pressure and 4·2° K.

The sample to be investigated may be placed in thermal contact with the high pressure container or may be immersed in a further small quantity of helium liquefied with the aid of the liquid in the container. In most of the liquefiers of this type the amount of liquid helium produced in one expansion has generally been in the range 50–200 cm.³. However, larger liquefiers have been made in which 1–1·5 litres can be produced per expansion and can be siphoned into another vessel. The only reason why a liquefier producing, say, 100 litres in a single expansion has not been constructed is that it has so far proved impossible to produce a metal from which the large high-pressure container can be forged and which does not become brittle at low temperatures.

## The Manipulation of Liquefied Gases and the Maintenance of Low Temperatures

Liquefied gases can be stored in the now familiar vacuum vessels (or Dewar vessels) of glass or metal with relatively little loss by evapora-

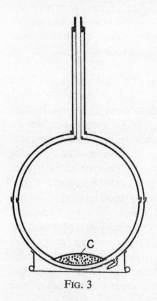

Fig. 3

tion. A typical vacuum flask is shown in Fig. 3. The charcoal C serves to adsorb the residual gases in the vacuum space and so maintain an adequately high vacuum ($10^{-5}$ mm. Hg or better). The long narrow neck of thin-walled tubing of low thermal conductivity (nickel-silver, monel, inconel) minimizes loss by conduction. Such vessels will preserve liquid air for many days, the loss with a good 25-litre flask being about 5 per cent of the contents per day. Large containers, the contents of which are measured in hundreds or thousands of litres, have a still smaller rate of loss and in them the interspace need only be evacuated to $0 \cdot 1$–$1$ mm. Hg provided it is filled with a powdered insulator such as Santocel.

When liquid helium became available in relatively large quantities the problem of its storage had to be solved. After the work of Wexler and others successful storage vessels were designed. A metal vacuum flask is immersed in liquid nitrogen so that the outer surface and the neck joint are at 77° K., so greatly reducing losses by radiation and conduction. It is now possible to store liquid helium in a 25-litre flask with only a loss of 1 litre per week. The transport of liquid helium over large distances by road, rail or air now presents no special difficulties.

The problem of the storage of liquid hydrogen is, curiously enough, more difficult. Ordinary hydrogen gas at room temperature is a mixture of 25 per cent *para*-hydrogen and 75 per cent *ortho*-hydrogen (see Chapter IV). This can be liquefied without appreciably changing the *o–p* ratio but if the liquid is stored the *ortho* is slowly converted into *para* with the liberation of the heat of conversion of 321 cal./mole. Since the latent heat of evaporation of hydrogen is about 217 cal./mole the conversion will result in a considerable loss of liquid by evaporation. Thus Grilly has shown that with a 25-litre vacuum vessel protected with liquid nitrogen as mentioned above the final evaporation rate due to the container was 22 cm.$^3$ per hour, whereas the initial rate when 71 per cent of *ortho*-hydrogen was present was as high as 270 cm.$^3$ per hour. It is therefore advantageous to convert the hydrogen to a lower *ortho* percentage (30–50 per cent) with the aid of a catalyst (a solid paramagnetic compound) placed in the liquid receiver of the hydrogen liquefier.

In the case of liquid hydrogen and helium it is essential to prevent air coming into contact with the liquid as otherwise the flask will rapidly fill with solidified air. The flask is therefore closed with a metal cap provided with an inlet and outlet for the liquid and an outlet for the vapour produced by the evaporation of the liquid. The liquid is then transferred to any apparatus to be filled by blowing it over with an excess pressure of the same gas from a cylinder with a reducing valve or from a rubber balloon in which the vapour has been allowed to collect by temporarily closing the vapour exit. The connection between the supply flask and the apparatus is best made with a tube, glass or metal, which is itself vacuum-jacketed to reduce loss by evaporation. Liquefied gases can be applied in various ways to the maintenance of low temperatures. In one type of cryostat (or low temperature thermostat) a bath of some liquid which does not solidify at the low temperatures required is cooled by means of liquid air and the temperature adjusted, if necessary, by means of an electric current in a heating coil. Thus in the Henning cryostat, Fig. 4, pentane contained in a vacuum vessel is cooled by a slow stream of liquid air through the porcelain U-tube G. A stirrer keeps the pentane in motion and serves to maintain a uniform temperature. The temperature of the bath is determined by the rate of flow of the liquid air into G and can be kept constant to a few hundredths of a degree over the range 120–273° K. Other cryostats of this type differ in the mode of application of the liquid air to the cooling pentane bath. The disadvantage of these cryostats is the danger of explosion of the very inflammable pentane but this can be avoided for the higher temperatures 190–273° K. by the use of a non-inflammable mixture of carbon tetrachloride and chloroform.

A further type of cryostat employs a regulated stream of cooled gas as the refrigerating agent. Thus hydrogen may be passed through a bath of liquid air into the vacuum vessel containing the experimental apparatus using an arrangement similar to that of Fig. 6, and temperatures down to 90° K. maintained constant. The chief limitation of such a cryostat is the small heat capacity of the gas.

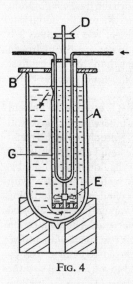

FIG. 4

The most highly developed method of obtaining accurately controlled low temperatures is that of immersing the apparatus directly in a bath of some pure liquefied gas. The liquid is stirred and the pressure at which it is boiling is accurately controlled. The pressure range usually employed is that from atmospheric pressure downwards so that any temperature from the normal boiling-point to the triple-point can be obtained. For this purpose the vacuum vessel containing the liquid is closed by some suitable cap to exclude air and to enable the pressure to be reduced. The vapour from the evaporating liquid passes either direct to a gas-holder (or the outer air) or through a needle-valve and a vacuum pump to the gas-holder. When the desired pressure has been reached it can be maintained constant by manipulating the needle-valve in accordance with the indications of a sensitive oil-manometer.† With adequate stirring the temperature can be obtained with sufficient accuracy for many purposes from the

† Or automatically by means of one of the many manostatic devices available.

reading of the manometer, using the known data for the vapour pressure-temperature curve.

The most commonly employed liquefied gases† are contained in Table 1, together with their boiling-points and triple-points. In the absence of special facilities for the purpose any of these gases, from methyl chloride to nitrogen, can be liquefied when required with the aid of liquid air.

TABLE 1

| Substance | Boiling-point (°K.) | Triple-point temperature (°K.) | Triple-point pressure (cm.) |
|---|---|---|---|
| Methyl chloride | 249·0 | 169·5 | |
| Nitrous oxide | 183·3 | 170·7 | |
| Ethylene | 169·4 | 104·1 | |
| Methane | 101·7 | 90·0 | 7·0 |
| Oxygen | 90·2 | 54·7 | 0·13 |
| Nitrogen | 77·3 | 63·3 | 9·6 |
| Hydrogen | 20·4 | 13·9 | 5·4 |
| Helium 4 | 4·2 | | |
| Helium 3 | 3·2 | | |

It will be seen that the range of temperature from 249·0° K. to 54·7° K. can be completely covered. There are, however, gaps between oxygen and hydrogen (54·7° K. to 20·4° K.) and between hydrogen and helium (13·9–4·2° K.) which cannot be completely bridged by any liquid.

Fig. 5 illustrates the employment of this method for the determination of the dielectric constant of liquid helium (Keesom and

† Solid carbon dioxide, either dry or mixed with alcohol, ether or acetone, is often used as a refrigerating agent giving a temperature of 194·6° K. The constancy of the temperature of apparatus immersed in such a cooling agent is not, however, as good as with a liquefied gas.

Wolfke). The experimental condenser C is immersed in the bath of liquid helium contained in the innermost vacuum vessel. The liquid is stirred by the magnetically operated stirrer S and is surrounded by baths of liquid hydrogen and liquid air to reduce the

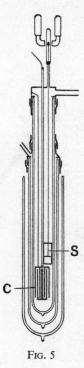

heat entry as much as possible. The helium and hydrogen vessels are closed at the top as shown.

The gap between 54·7° K. and 20·4° K. has been bridged by Kamerlingh Onnes and Crommelin by means of a hydrogen vapour cryostat shown diagrammatically in Fig. 6. Hydrogen from a cylinder passes through the coil C immersed in liquid hydrogen in the vacuum vessel I and is cooled to about 20° K. It then passes through a vacuum-jacketed tube into the vacuum vessel II where it encounters an electrical heater E. Its temperature is there raised to that at which the experimental apparatus in II has to be maintained. The rate of flow of the gas can be adjusted to the desired value and with automatic regulation of the heating current supplemented, if required, by hand regulation by an observer watching the galvanometer in the circuit of a resistance thermometer in II, a constancy of 0·01° K. can be obtained.

The gap 13·9–4·2° K. could similarly be bridged by some form of helium vapour cryostat. When the pressure above liquid hydrogen is reduced below 5 cm. the hydrogen solidifies and by further reducing the pressure the temperature of the solid can be reduced to as low as 10° K. For certain purposes it is possible to employ solid hydrogen as the cooling agent.

Fig. 5

## The Production of Temperatures below 1° K.

Since the lowest pressure which can readily be maintained over liquid helium with the aid of a mechanical pump is about 0·2 mm. Hg, the temperature to which this pressure corresponds, 1·1° K., is the lowest at which it is generally possible to carry out experiments in the various cryogenic laboratories. Temperatures lower than $1.1°$ K. may be obtained by the use of special apparatus and methods.

With the aid of large diffusion pumps, preferably the booster type with a pumping speed of many hundreds of litres per sec., it is possible to reduce the vapour pressure of the helium to between $2 \times 10^{-3}$ and $10^{-2}$ mm. Hg and so to reduce the temperature to between $0.7$ and $0.8°$ K. Precautions must be taken to prevent room temperature radiation from the cryostat cap reaching the liquid helium and to reduce the loss of liquid due to the creeping film (see Chapter III).

Since the lighter isotope of helium $He^3$ has a much higher vapour pressure than $He^4$ at corresponding temperatures, it became an attractive proposition to use $He^3$ as a cryostat liquid to obtain temperatures below $1°$ K. Several designs have been published which provide a liquid bath of a few cm.$^3$ volume. In the most advanced design the evaporated $He^3$ is reliquefied with the aid of liquid $He^4$ and returned to the cryostat. By reducing the vapour pressure of the $He^3$ to $1.5 \times 10^{-3}$ mm. Hg a temperature of $0.3°$ K. can be obtained.

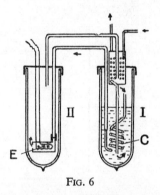

Fig. 6

The problem of obtaining temperatures well below $1°$ K. has, however, been solved in quite a different way. In 1926 it was suggested independently by Giauque and by Debye that if a paramagnetic salt were magnetized isothermally in a strong magnetic field at say, $1°$ K., insulated thermally and then demagnetized adiabatically, the temperature of the salt would fall appreciably, perhaps to $0.01°$ K. A thermodynamic treatment of the problem gives the formula

$$\left(\frac{\partial T}{\partial H}\right)_s = -\frac{T}{C_H}\left(\frac{\partial \sigma}{\partial T}\right)_H$$

for the rate of change of temperature with applied magnetic field, where $C_H$ is the specific heat at constant $H$ and $(\partial\sigma/\partial T)_H$ is the rate of change of magnetization with temperature at constant $H$. The effect

2

can, however, be more readily understood in terms of the variation of the entropy of the salt with temperature and magnetic field. Consider a paramagnetic salt which follows Curie's law closely at the higher temperatures. At 1° K. the part of the entropy due to the thermal motions of the atoms is almost negligibly small compared with that due to the random distribution of the atomic moments of the un-magnetized salt (A of Fig. 7). If now the salt is magnetized isotherm-ally at 1° K. a considerable degree of order (parallelism) is introduced into the distribution of the atomic moments and the entropy falls to

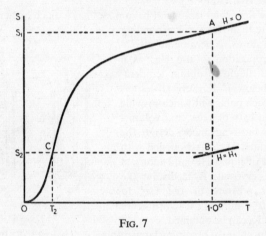

Fig. 7

B. On the other hand, the entropy of the unmagnetized salt must, by the third law of thermodynamics, fall to zero at the Absolute Zero. The mechanism for this fall in entropy is provided by the interaction of the atomic magnetic moments with (i) the electrostatic field of the surrounding ions, and (ii) with each other. The variation of the entropy with temperature is then given by the curve ($H = 0$) in Fig. 7. Starting from B with a temperature of 1° K., and a magnetic field of 10,000–30,000 oe. and demagnetizing adiabatically to $H = 0$, the point C is reached, the temperature falling to $T_2$. It is obvious that the lower the temperature at which the entropy for $H = 0$ begins to decrease rapidly, the lower will be the final temperature after demagnetization.

Such adiabatic demagnetizations were first achieved experimentally by Giauque and MacDougall and by de Haas, Kramers and Wiersma, followed somewhat later by Simon and Kurti. The paramagnetic salt, preferably in the form of an ellipsoid or a sphere of compressed powder, is suspended by fine threads inside a cylindrical container which is cooled to about 1° K. The whole is placed between the poles of a powerful electromagnet or inside an iron-free solenoid of the type developed by Bitter. With a small pressure of helium gas in the container, a magnetic field is applied, the heat of magnetization is conducted away to the liquid helium bath and the container is then evacuated to a high vacuum. The paramagnetic salt is now magnetized at 1° K. and is thermally insulated from its surroundings. The adiabatic demagnetization is usually carried out by withdrawing the salt and its associated equipment from the magnet or solenoid to a position where the magnetic field is zero or has some small known value. Some device for measuring the susceptibility of the salt is always included so that the low temperature reached after demagnetization can be determined.† For this purpose primary and secondary coils are usually wound on the outside of the container. Measurement of the e.m.f. induced in the secondary on reversal of a known current in the primary provides the data for the determination of the susceptibility and hence of the temperature from Curie's law, $\chi T^* = $ const., where $\chi = $ susceptibility of the salt and $T^* = $ 'Curie temperature'. The choice of the paramagnetic salt to be used is a matter of some importance. If the purpose is to produce as low a temperature as possible then it is necessary to choose a salt with the sharp drop in the $S - T$ ($H = 0$) curve at as low a temperature as possible. If the purpose is to cool some other substance and maintain an approximately constant temperature as long as possible then the choice is on a salt in which a maximum of the specific heat or a sharp drop in the $S - T$ ($H = 0$) curve, since $C = T(dS/dT)$, occurs near the desired temperature.

A low temperature for the fall in entropy is caused by the smallness of the interaction between the magnetic moments of the ions themselves and between the magnetic moments and the crystal lattice. The direct dipole–dipole interaction and the 'exchange interaction' of quantum mechanics can be made small by using a 'magnetically dilute' salt such as iron ammonium alum in which the magnetic ions

† The 'magnetic thermometer' is discussed in more detail in Chapter II.

are kept at a large distance apart by the outer (diamagnetic) constituents of the molecule. This dilution can be further increased by crystallizing together the paramagnetic iron alum with the isomorphous aluminium alum so that there is, say, one molecule of the former to twenty of the latter.

The interaction with the electrical field of the crystal lattice can be made small by choosing a salt whose magnetic moment is due actually or effectively only to electronic spin as the interaction is much smaller for these ions than for those in which orbital magnetic moment is also present.† Gadolinium sulphate, manganese ammonium sulphate, titanium caesium alum, iron ammonium alum and chromium potassium alum satisfy these conditions and the two latter salts in particular have been used extensively for adiabatic demagnetization.

The earliest published experiments resulted in the production of a temperature of $0.25°$ K., while the lowest temperature obtained by a single-stage demagnetization stands at present at $0.0014°$ K. (de Klerk, Steenland and Gorter, 1950).

For the demagnetization technique to be really useful, it must be possible to cool other substances by it and to maintain the very low temperatures approximately constant over a period long enough for physical measurements to be made. Several factors are involved: the paramagnetic salt should have a high specific heat, there should be as small a heat influx as possible, some means must be available for making thermal contact between the paramagnetic salt and the other material to be cooled and the cooling, which first takes place in the spin system of the paramagnetic salt, must be transmitted to the lattice in a time short compared with the duration of any proposed experiment.

Fortunately the paramagnetic salts possess the required high specific heat and in this respect paramagnetic demagnetization has a great advantage over all other possible methods for the production of temperatures below $1°$ K. The heat capacity of 1 gm. of iron ammonium alum at $0.05°$ K. is the same as that of 25,000 gm. of copper or 2 litres of liquid helium.

The heat influx can be made very small at these temperatures. There is no appreciable contribution due to radiation from the container walls as the latter are at about $1°$ K. nor through the residual gas in the

† See Chapter VI.

container as the vapour pressure of helium at these very low temperatures is quite negligible.† Conduction down the silk or nylon fibre suspensions can be kept very low and the main source of heat is the continuous condensation on the salt of helium desorbed from the walls of the container. Cooke and Hull (1942) by a special 'guard ring' arrangement of three samples of paramagnetic salt, succeeded in reducing the heat influx into the middle one to 1 erg/min. Without special precautions the heat can still be kept down to 5 erg/min.

The production of a good thermal contact between the paramagnetic salt and any solid body, which is to be cooled, is a rather difficult problem. Conduction through the salt is itself, even though it has been compressed almost to the density of the actual crystals, is very poor at the lowest temperatures. For some purposes the substance to be cooled can be mixed with the paramagnetic salt and the whole compressed into a cylindrical or ellipsoidal shape. The method was used by Kurti and Simon for the detection of superconductivity in zirconium, cadmium and hafnium below 1° K. The method is, however, obviously only of limited applicability. A more satisfactory method (Mendoza 1948, Mendoza and Thomas, 1951) is to embed parallel strips of copper in the compressed salt and attach the material under investigation to the protruding ends of the copper. It can be arranged that the temperature difference between the material and the paramagnetic salt is not greater than $\frac{1}{1000}°$ down to 0·1° K. At lower temperatures however the temperature difference would increase rapidly.

The obvious solution of using liquid helium to make the thermal contact presents difficulties on account of the film of liquid helium which covers all surfaces in contact with the liquid below 2·17° K. and which creeps up any pumping tube and evaporates at a place where the temperature is high enough.‡ If the pumping tube is wide there will be a back-diffusion of the helium vapour which will condense on the cold paramagnetic salt so producing a high heat influx. Hudson, Hunt and Kurti have overcome the difficulty by placing the salt, specimen and liquid helium in a cylindrical vessel connected by a length of 0·2 mm. inside diameter capillary to the pumping tube which

† The calculated vapour pressure of helium at 0·1° K. is $3·4 \times 10^{-33}$ and at 0·01° K. $3 \times 10^{-314}$ mm. Hg.

‡ See Chapter III.

is kept at 0·9° K. The amount of helium creeping out via the film is now small as the volume creeping per second is proportional to the perimeter of the fine capillary and a pump with a speed of several litres per second can remove the evaporated film sufficiently fast to ensure that back-diffusion is very small. A heat influx of 500–1000 ergs/min. can be achieved with a warming time from 0·05–0·9° K. of about $1\frac{1}{2}$ hours. The liquid helium must, however, be kept down to a fairly thin layer as the very high heat transport possible in the neighbourhood of 1·5° K. has diminished enormously at 0·1° K. Kurti calculates that a layer of liquid helium 0·1 mm. thick can transmit 100 ergs/min. per cm.$^2$ at 0·05° K. for a temperature difference of 0·001 deg.

Another method is to enclose the salt and specimen in a metal capsule filled at room temperature with helium gas at a pressure of 100 atm. and sealed off. The helium condenses at the low temperatures and provides the required thermal contact between the salt and the specimen.

The rate, at which a change in the energy of the spin system is transferred to the lattice, fortunately presents no problem for adiabatic demagnetization. The spin system itself returns to equilibrium very rapidly after a disturbance, the rate being governed by the so-called spin–spin relaxation time which is of the order of $10^{-10}$ sec. independent of temperature. It is, however, not *a priori* necessary that a change in the energy of the spin system will be communicated to the lattice in a short time. Thus immediately after a demagnetization there will be a new equilibrium in the spin system corresponding to a low spin temperature $T_s$ but the lattice temperature $T_L$ will initially have the same value as before the demagnetization. The time for the cooling of the lattice to a new low temperature is found experimentally to be at most a matter of seconds. If the first theoretical predictions regarding the spin–lattice relaxation time which gave values of the order of $10^6$ sec. for $T_s = 0·01°$ K. had proved to be correct, adiabatic demagnetization would have possessed little practical value. Later investigations by Kronig (1939) and van Vleck (1940), in which the transference of energy from the spin system to the lattice takes place through the spin–orbit coupling, have given relaxation times of the order of those actually observed.

After demagnetization the temperature of the paramagnetic salt and any system in thermal contact with the latter rises as a result of the unavoidable influx of heat. The 'warming time' during which the system rises to $1.0°$ K. may vary from half an hour to several hours and the experiments must be carried out during this period of slowly rising temperature. It would be desirable to have available a system in which strictly constant temperatures below $1°$ K. can be maintained in spite of relatively large heat influxes. Before the advent of the liquid-helium-three cryostat, the problem was solved by the introduction of the 'magnetic refrigerator' by Daunt and Heer. This was made possible by the development of the 'thermal valve', a device by means of which thermal contact can be made or broken reliably at will at temperatures between $1°$ K. and $0.1°$ K. The thermal link consists of a wire or strip of superconducting material such as lead or niobium. The thermal conductivity of these metals in the superconducting state is very much smaller than it is in the normal state at the

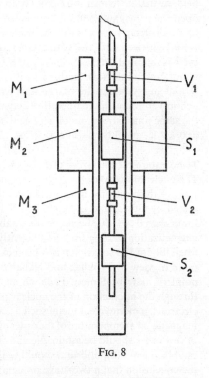

FIG. 8

same temperature, the ratio $K_n/K_s$ being of the order of 1000. So if the superconductivity of the thermal link is destroyed by the application of a magnetic field of the order of several hundreds of oersteds, the thermal conduction through the link is good but when the magnetic field is removed the conduction falls to a very small value. In the magnetic refrigerator two samples of paramagnetic salt, $S_1$, the working substance, ferric ammonium alum and, $S_2$, the reservoir, chromium potassium alum, are connected to one another and to the outer helium bath at $1.1°$ K. by means of the thermal valves $V_1$ and $V_2$ as shown in Fig. 8. With valve $V_1$ open and valve $V_2$ closed the salt $S_1$ is magnetized and the heat of magnetization is conducted to the helium bath, then with both valves closed the salt $S_1$ is demagnetized but not to zero field, so that its temperature falls. With valve $V_1$ closed and valve $V_2$ open the demagnetization is completed while heat flows almost isothermally from salt $S_2$ to salt $S_1$. Then with both valves closed salt $S_1$ is remagnetized until the bath temperature is reached and the whole cycle is repeated. In practice, the cycle is carried out automatically at about 2-min. intervals. In this way it is possible to maintain the salt $S_2$ and any system in thermal contact with it (such as a bath of liquid helium) at a constant temperature between $1°$ K. and $0.25°$ K. and at the same time extract amounts of heat corresponding to 290 erg/sec. at $0.45°$ K. and 70 erg/sec. at $0.26°$ K.

## Temperatures of the Order of $10^{-6°}$ K.

The nuclei of many atoms possess magnetic moments of the order of $\frac{1}{1000}$ of the electronic moments of paramagnetics.† It has been suggested by Gorter and by Kurti and Simon that temperatures much lower than $0.001°$ K. should be obtainable by the aid of a nuclear demagnetization starting from a sufficiently low initial temperature. The feasibility of the suggestion has been examined from the theoretical point of view by Fröhlich and Nabarro and from the experimental point of view by Simon. Fröhlich and Nabarro have shown that through the interaction of the nuclear moments with the conduction electrons, a monovalent metal such as copper should become 'ferromagnetic' at a temperature of the order of $10^{-6°}$ K., that temperatures of this order should be attainable and that the time required for the establishment of equilibrium should be less than 1 sec. Simon came to the conclusion that a two-stage process using a paramagnetic salt to cool a specimen of copper to $0.01°$ K., magnetizing the copper at $0.01°$ K. and demagnetizing to produce temperatures of the order of $10^{-6°}$ K. should not present any insuperable experimental difficulties.

The problems to be solved are two-fold: (i) the production of sufficiently high magnetic fields, of the order of 100,000 oe., for the

† See Tolansky, *Hyperfine Structure in Line Spectra and Nuclear Spin*, Methuen's Monographs on Physical Subjects.

nuclear stage, and (ii) the making, and later, breaking of heat contact between the two stages.

The first successful nuclear demagnetization was carried out by Kurti, Robinson, Simon and Spohr in 1956 at the Clarendon Laboratory, Oxford. The first stage was chromic potassium alum with 1500 enamelled copper wires of 0·1 mm. diameter embedded in it. The nuclear stage was the lower end of the same wires folded to make a compact sample. Demagnetization of the first stage cooled the nuclear stage to 0·012° K. at which the latter was magnetized in fields up to 28,000 oe. The whole system was surrounded by thermal shields at 20° K., 4° K., 1° K. and 0·1° K., the last temperature being obtained by the demagnetization of manganese ammonium sulphate. No attempt was made to isolate the nuclear stage after the magnetization and the link through the copper wires remained unbroken after demagnetization, so that the lowest temperature obtained was held only for a short time. No doubt a superconducting thermal valve can be included in later experiments with reasonable hopes of success.

The curve of temperature of the nuclear stage after demagnetization was plotted as a function of the time. Extrapolation backwards to zero time showed that the lowest temperature obtained with 28,000 oe. was about $17 \times 10^{-6°}$ K. The temperature rose to $10^{-4°}$ K. in 50 sec. and to $5 \times 10^{-4°}$ K. in 100 sec.

The work has been carried a stage further by Hobden and Kurti (1959) who modified the apparatus by the substitution of a liquid helium three bath at 0·35° K. for the manganese ammonium sulphate shield at 0·1° K. This made it possible to measure the temperature of the first stage more accurately. The lowest temperature reached was $1·2 \times 10^{-6°}$ K.

This achievement is thus the first step into a new and very intriguing region of low temperatures where some day microdegrees Kelvin may be as familiar as millidegrees are today.

## Other Possible Methods for the Production of Very Low Temperatures

*Simon desorption method.* A method depending on the desorption of helium gas adsorbed on charcoal at temperatures obtained with solid hydrogen has been developed by Simon for the production of helium temperatures and where necessary the liquefaction of helium on a small scale.† For the latter purpose it was superseded by the more convenient single expansion method but can still serve a useful purpose in the production of temperatures in the difficult region between 10° K. and 4·2° K. (and using hydrogen gas and solid nitrogen in place of helium and solid hydrogen, in the other difficult region between 55° K. and 20° K.).

*Adiabatic magnetization of a superconductor.* Since the entropy of a metal in the superconducting state (see Chapter V) is less than that in the normal state at the same temperature, an adiabatic application of a magnetic field large enough to destroy superconductivity will cool the metal. It can be calculated that, with an initial temperature of 1° K., a final temperature of 0·1° K. or rather lower should be obtained and such coolings have been observed by Mendelssohn and Moore and by Keesom and Kok. Since the magnetic fields required are only a few hundreds of oersteds a much larger volume can be cooled than in paramagnetic demagnetization. However, the superconductor method is not capable of cooling external systems to the same extent as the paramagnetic method as the specific heat of the superconductor is small at very low temperatures. Mendelssohn has, however, recently suggested that magnetization of a superconductor can be profitably employed in the temperature region between 0·3° K. and 1° K. where the paramagnetic method is less suitable than at lower temperatures. The superconductors with high transition temperature and high Debye $\theta$ (see Chapter IV) would be chosen, as their specific heats would be favourable.

*Passage of liquid helium II through a porous plug.* It has been shown by Mendelssohn and Daunt and by Kapitza that if liquid helium at any temperature below 2·17° K. is made to flow adiabatically through a fine capillary or a series of minute openings such as a porous plug, an appreciable drop in temperature of the emerging liquid occurs for relatively small pressure drops. Kapitza has suggested the process as a means of producing temperatures below 1° K. using a regenerative method to obtain progressive cooling. Preliminary experiments giving a temperature drop of 0·3° K. have been reported. However, Simon has shown that any method which uses liquid helium (He[4]) as the

† A description of the method is to be found in the first edition of this book. See also Burton *et al.* (p. 28), Ruhemann (p. 47) and Keesom (p. 158) in the Bibliography.

refrigerant cannot be used to cool any appreciable mass of other material to very low temperatures as the entropy of the liquid is negligibly small below $1°$ K. Thus, Simon has calculated that the heat content for a paramagnetic salt with a specific heat anomaly at $0.1°$ K. is $8 \times 10^{-5}$ cal. per cm.$^3$ in the temperature range $0.005-0.02°$ K. while that of liquid helium is $10^{-11}$ cal. over the same temperature range.

*Use of solutions of He$^3$ for obtaining temperatures below $1°$ K.* An interesting suggestion has been made by H. London for obtaining very low temperatures by means of a solution of the rarer isotope He$_3$ in the commoner isotope He$^4$. In any dilute solution the solute molecules can be considered to behave like a gas whose pressure is the osmotic pressure and whose volume is the volume of the solution. Dilution of the solution by adding more solvent causes an 'expansion' of the solute 'gas', if this dilution is carried out reversibly and adiabatically (for instance, by flow through a semi-permeable membrane) a cooling should result.

The adiabatic dilution of solutions of He$^3$ in He$^4$, starting from $1°$ K. should result in the production of lower temperatures. He$^3$ obeys Fermi-Dirac statistics so that at high concentrations it behaves like a degenerate Fermi-Dirac gas and has a specific heat proportional to $T$; at low concentrations it behaves classically and its specific heat is $\frac{3}{2}R$. The result is that the specific heat and entropy of the He$^3$, even in very dilute solutions, greatly exceed those of the He$^4$ below $1°$ K. and the presence of He$^4$ can be ignored. Further, an adiabatic dilution should follow the law $Tv^{2/3} = $ const., in both concentrated and dilute solutions. Hence an expansion of volume by a factor 1000 should cause the temperature to fall by a factor 100, with the removal of a considerable amount of entropy. Experiments designed to test the idea have been described by London, Mendoza and Clarke. A container with a He$^3$-He$^4$ solution at temperature $T_1$ communicated through a *superleak*† with another container filled with He$^4$ at temperature $T_2$. The observations confirmed the feasibility of the proposed cooling method for producing temperatures in the neighbourhood of $0.1°$ K.

† A *superleak* is a very narrow channel through which the *superfluid* component of liquid He$^4$ can flow readily but the *normal* component cannot (see Chapter III).

## CHAPTER II

# The Measurement of Low Temperatures

## The Gas Thermometer and its Corrections

The measurement of any low temperature in an experiment is almost invariably carried out with the aid of some suitable secondary thermometer. The determination therefore involves two processes, the actual measurement of the low temperature and the calibration of the thermometer. For this calibration the temperature of certain 'fixed points' must have been determined previously with the aid of a standard instrument, preferably on the thermodynamic scale.

Standard measurements of low temperatures are made almost exclusively with the constant volume gas thermometer, generally filled to a pressure of 1000 mm. Hg at 0° C. with hydrogen or helium. The temperature scale so obtained is known as the normal hydrogen (or helium) scale.

The temperatures are deduced from the observed pressure of the gas in the thermometer from the relation

$$t_v = \frac{p_{t_v} - p_0}{p_{100} - p_0} \times 100$$

or

$$p_{t_v} = p_0(1 + \alpha t_v) = p_0 \alpha T_v$$

in which $p_{t_v}$, $p_{100}$, $p_0$ are the pressures at $t_v$, 100° C. and 0° C., $\alpha =$ coefficient of increase of pressure with temperature, $t_v =$ Celsius temperature and $T_v =$ absolute temperature.

The observed pressure must be corrected for the thermal expansion of the bulb of the thermometer, for the change in volume of the bulb with internal pressure, for the fact that the 'dead space' (the volume enclosed between the fixed meniscus of the mercury in the manometer and the top of the thermometer bulb) is not at the temperature to be measured and for the variation of the dead space with temperature. The normal hydrogen scale so obtained can be employed down to 23° K. and the helium scale down to about 4° K.

For the measurement of 'helium temperatures', say, 4·2–0·9° K., with the gas thermometer the zero-point pressure must be chosen much smaller than 1000 mm. and helium at pressures from 10 cm. to 0·2 cm. at 0° C. is used. The pressures observed at helium temperatures are then so small that the mercury manometer usually employed is replaced by a Pirani or hot wire manometer, in which the pressure is deduced from the resistance of a fine wire exposed to the gas. The main uncertainty in the measurement of these very low temperatures lies in the fact that a correction has to be applied for the thermal molecular difference of pressure. When two bulbs, containing gas at such a low pressure that the mean free path of the molecules is comparable or large compared with the diameter of the connecting tube, are at different temperatures there is a difference in pressure between them known as the thermal molecular pressure. Since a complete theoretical treatment of this effect is not yet available there is some uncertainty in the value of the correction to be applied in the thermometry of very low temperatures to allow for the fact that the bulb is at the low temperature and the hot wire manometer at 0° C. Different thermometers after the correction has been applied agree, however, to within about 0·01°.

The readings of the gas thermometer can be corrected so as to give absolute or thermodynamical temperatures provided the equation of state of the thermometric gas is sufficiently well known. Thus it can be shown that a gas thermometer containing an 'ideal gas', i.e. a gas obeying the law $pv = R\theta$, would give readings directly on Kelvin's thermodynamical scale of temperature. It is also known that any real gas approaches the ideal gas in its properties more closely the lower the pressure. If then the readings of any real gas thermometer are extrapolated to the limit of vanishingly small pressure, the scale so obtained will agree with the ideal gas scale. This extrapolation can be carried out as follows:

The equation of state of any real gas can be written in the form

$$pv = A + Bp + Cp^2 + \ldots \tag{1}$$

or
$$pv = A + B/v + C/v^2 + \ldots \tag{2}$$

in which $A$, $B$, $C$ are functions of the temperature. In expression (1) if the unit of pressure is 1 m. of mercury, then $B/A$ is of the order $10^{-3}$ and $C/A$ $10^{-5}$ to $10^{-6}$.

Taking expression (1) and neglecting the terms involving $C$, we can write for the case of the constant volume thermometer at temperatures $t$, 100° and 0°

$$p_0 v_0 = A_0 + B_0 p_0$$

$$p_{100} v_0 = A_{100} + B_{100} p_{100}$$

$$p_t v_0 = A_t + B_t p_t$$

The gas scale temperature $t_v$ is given by

$$t_v = 100 \frac{p_t - p_0}{p_{100} - p_0} = 100 \left\{ \frac{A_t - A_0 + B_t p_t - B_0 p_0}{A_{100} - A_0 + B_{100} p_{100} - B_0 p_0} \right\}$$

and the corresponding temperature for the limit $p \to 0$ is obviously

$$t(\lim) = 100 \frac{A_t - A_0}{A_{100} - A_0}$$

since the gas in the limiting case $p \to 0$ follows the law $pv = A$. The difference between $t_v$ and $t(\lim)$ is then the correction to be applied to $t_v$ to extrapolate to $p \to 0$.

Subtracting the two expressions above, expanding by the Binomial Theorem and neglecting terms in $(Bp_0/A)^2$ we obtain

$$t(\lim) - t_v = t(\lim) \left\{ \frac{B_{100} p_{100} - B_0 p_0}{A_{100} - A_0} - \frac{B_t p_t - B_0 p_0}{A_t - A_0} \right\}$$

Thus, provided the values of $A$ and $B$ are known from determinations of the isotherms of the thermometric gas, we can calculate the corrections to be applied to the readings of any gas thermometer to convert them into thermodynamic temperatures. It will be seen that the correction itself contains $t(\lim)$ as shown above. In using the formula the uncorrected value $t_v$ is first inserted in the right-hand side of the equation and a value of the correction obtained. This correction is then applied and the corrected value of $t(\lim)$ inserted in the formula, so deriving a second approximation of the value of the correction.

It has been found that the scales of all gas thermometers corrected in the above way agree with each other to within the accuracy claimed for the measurements and with the thermodynamic scale obtained in other ways, for example, from observations on the Joule-Thomson effect.†

The magnitude of the corrections may be judged from the values given in Table 2 for the constant volume $H_2$ and He thermometers with a zero-point pressure of 1000 mm. Hg derived from the measurements of Holborn and Otto and of Onnes and Cath.

The corrections to be applied in the temperature range $4 \cdot 2°$–$0 \cdot 9°$ K. when the zero-point pressure is 10 cm. or less are smaller than the errors of observation and can be neglected.

TABLE 2

| $t$ (°C.) | $H_2$ | He |
|:---:|:---:|:---:|
| 0 | 0·00 | 0·00 |
| −50 | +0·006 | +0·003 |
| −100 | +0·015 | +0·008 |
| −150 | +0·027 | +0·014 |
| −200 | +0·069 | +0·020 |
| −250 | +0·135 | +0·037 |

For the limiting case of infinitely small pressure the scales of the constant volume and constant pressure thermometers are the same and agree with that given by the expression

$$\lim_{p \to 0} (pv)_t = \lim_{p \to 0} (pv)_0 (1 + \gamma t)$$

$$= \lim_{p \to 0} (pv)_0 \gamma T$$

when
$$T = 1/\gamma + t$$

$1/\gamma$ is then the temperature of the ice-point on the thermodynamic scale. A consideration of all available data gave $273 \cdot 15°$ K. as the

† For a description of the method of correcting the gas thermometer to the thermodynamic scale with the aid of the Joule-Thomson effect see, for example, Roberts, *Heat and Thermodynamics*.

temperature of the ice-point. However, it was agreed in 1954 to re-define the absolute thermodynamic scale in terms of absolute zero, 0° K., and one upper standard fixed point. For this the temperature of the triple point of water is chosen rather than the ice-point as it is more accurately reproducible. This temperature is defined as 273·16° K. (0·01° C.). The temperature of the ice-point then still 273·15° K. (0° C.) but it is no longer used as a fundamental point for the definition of the temperature scale.

With the aid of the gas thermometer, corrected as above, the tem-peratures of the following thermometric fixed points have been determined for the purpose of calibrating secondary thermometers; melting-point of mercury (−38·87° C.), the sublimation-point of solid carbon dioxide (−78·51° C. at 1 atm. pressure), the boiling-point of oxygen (−182·97° C.), the boiling-point of normal† hydrogen (−252·76° C.).

## Secondary Thermometers

(a) *Resistance thermometers*. The platinum resistance thermometer can be employed to measure temperatures down to about 15° K., below which it becomes insensitive.

Various formulae have been proposed for the determination of the temperature in the range 273–80° K. from the observed resistance, the most satisfactory formula being that of Van Dusen

$$t = \frac{R_t - R_0}{\alpha R_0} + \delta\left(\frac{t}{100}\right)\left(\frac{t}{100} - 1\right) + \beta\left(\frac{t}{100}\right)^3\left(\frac{t}{100} - 1\right)$$

where $t$ = temperature on the International Celsius Scale, $R_t$ = re-sistance at temperature $t$ and $\alpha, \delta, \beta$ = constants.

The constants in the above equation can be deduced by calibrating the thermometer at the steam-point, the ice-point, the melting-point of mercury and the boiling-point of oxygen.

Formulae have been proposed whereby the temperature can be derived from the observed resistance in the temperature range 90–20° K. but their general validity have yet to be established. The only quite reliable procedure is to compare the platinum thermometer directly (or indirectly via the vapour pressure thermometer) with the gas thermometer at as many points as possible in the range required.

† 75 per cent *ortho*-hydrogen, 25 per cent *para*-hydrogen.

Resistance thermometers of gold and lead can also be used at hydrogen temperatures with advantage. Since the electrical resistance of pure metals (apart from the occurrence of superconductivity, see Chapter V) becomes practically independent of the temperature in the region of helium temperatures, they cannot be employed as resistance thermometers in this region. However, the resistance of various alloys, such as manganin and constantan, which is nearly independent of the temperature at higher temperatures, decreases appreciably with decreasing temperature below 5° K. These alloys can therefore be used in resistance thermometers in this temperature range but the sensitivity is not high, the temperature coefficient being of the order of 0·001. They are not much affected by the presence of magnetic fields.

More sensitive thermometers for the range of temperature below 7° K. can be made by adding a small amount of lead (about 0·05 per cent) to phosphor bronze or brass. Wires are drawn from the alloy and used in the unannealed springy state. They then have a temperature coefficient of the order of 0·03 but the sensitivity varies with the diameter to which the wire has been drawn. The resistance of these thermometers depends on the strength of the measuring current and the magnitude of any magnetic field present. They have therefore to be calibrated for the circumstances in which they are to be used. Allen and Shire had shown that phosphor bronze thermometers can be used down to 0·03° K. The sensitivity to an external magnetic field can be greatly reduced by adding a small quantity of lead-bismuth alloy (25 per cent Bi) which has a very high critical magnetic field (see Chapter V, Superconductivity) but the sensitivity to measuring current still remains.

Carbon can also be used as a resistance thermometer at very low temperatures, the resistance increasing rapidly as the temperature decreases. Formerly it was used either as graphite or as a carbon ink line drawn on glass. More recently it has been found that certain commercial carbon composition resistors of the one watt size are very suitable for use in the temperature range 2–20° K. They are reasonably stable, adequately sensitive and unaffected by all but the strongest magnetic fields. It is also possible to construct carbon thermometers by coating a suitable size copper rod with a thin layer of varnish and then applying a coat of Aquadag and baking to 150° C. It is possible

3

to produce a thermometer of the desired resistance with high sensitivity in the desired portion of the temperature range between 20° K. and 0·03° K. by varying the consistency of the Aquadag and the thickness of the applied layer. A secondary thermometer which promises to be very useful when it becomes available commercially is the single crystal of arsenic-doped germanium described by Geballe and his co-workers. The resistance of one sample had the following values: 20° K., 9 ohms; 4° K., 155 ohms; 2° K., 1600 ohms; and the temperatures were reproducible to 0·001 deg. even after cycling many times between room temperature and 4° K. This degree of stability at helium temperatures is a very valuable feature.

(b) *Thermocouples*. Various thermocouples can be used for the measurement of low temperatures. Thus the copper–constantan couple can be employed down to 15° K. Nernst has published the following formula for the electromotive force of this couple for the range 100–15° K.

$$e = 31·22 \log (1 + T/90) + 1·0 \times 10^{-7} T^4 \text{ microvolts}$$

In the region of hydrogen temperatures the gold–silver couple, which gives practically no e.m.f. at room temperature, is more sensitive than the copper–constantan couple (Onnes and Clay). It has also been suggested by Keesom and Borelius that a couple of 1 at. per cent of Co in Au against 1 at. per cent of Au in Ag should be used for the measurement of very low temperatures. This couple gives the following approximate values of the thermoelectric power (microvolts per deg.) at 273° K., 37; 93° K., 34; 53° K., 28; 23° K., 17 and 18° K., 14. It should still give appreciable e.m.f.s at helium temperatures, and is likely to be generally suitable for the measurement of very low temperatures, particularly as such dilute alloys are likely to retain their calibration during use.

(c) *Vapour pressure thermometers*. The determination of the vapour pressure of a suitable liquid in equilibrium with its vapour provides a sensitive and convenient method for the measurement of low temperatures (Stock and Neilson). The substance, which must be gaseous at room temperature and liquid in the temperature range to be measured, is contained in a small bulb connected to a manometer. The bulb is placed in the apparatus where the temperature is to be determined and the pressure shown by the manometer is the saturated vapour pressure corresponding to the temperature of the coldest part of the thermometer.

A formula connecting the vapour pressure and the temperature can be obtained by integrating the Clausius-Clapeyron equation

$$\frac{dp}{dT} = \frac{L}{T(v_1 - v_2)}$$

($p$ = vapour pressure, $L$ = latent heat of vaporization, $v_1$, $v_2$ specific volumes of vapour and liquid respectively), using certain simplifying

TABLE 3

| Substance | Range (°K.) | $a$ | $c \times 10^3$ | $k$ |
|-----------|-------------|-----|-----------------|-----|
| $CS_2$ | 285 to 248 | 1682·38 | 5·2980 | 5·44706 |
| $NH_3$ | 238 to 193 | 1393·60 | 5·7034 | 5·89437 |
| $HCl$ | 186 to 155 | 905·53 | 5·0077 | 4·65491 |
| $C_2H_4$ | 163 to 132 | 834·13 | 8·3753 | 5·32089 |
| $CH_4$ | 111 to 103 | 472·47 | 9·6351 | 4·59825 |
| $O_2$ | 90 to 68 | 379·95 | 9·6219 | 4·53939 |

assumptions. The integration leads to a formula of the type below or a somewhat more complicated expression,

$$\log p = -\frac{a}{T} + b \log T - cT + k$$

in which $a$, $b$, $c$ and $k$ are constants.

Table 3 gives the values of the constants of some of the substances suitable for the determination of low temperatures. Following Nernst $b$ is taken as 1·75 and the unit of pressure is 1 m. of mercury.

The sensitivity of the vapour pressure thermometer is much greater than that of the gas thermometer, thus the vapour pressure of oxygen near its normal boiling-point changes by about 80 mm. Hg per deg., while with a constant volume gas thermometer with a zero-point pressure of 1000 mm. Hg the corresponding change is less than 4 mm. Hg per deg. in this temperature region.

Provided the bath of liquefied gas is adequately stirred it is frequently sufficient to determine the vapour pressure by means of a manometer attached to the exit tube of the apparatus in order to determine the temperature with an accuracy of $0 \cdot 1°$ or better.

The temperature of a bath of freshly prepared liquid hydrogen, i.e. normal hydrogen with 75 per cent $o$-$H_2$, 25 per cent $p$-$H_2$, can be deduced from the formula

$$\log_{10} p \text{ (mm.)} = 4 \cdot 66687 + 0 \cdot 020537T - 44 \cdot 9569/T$$

The boiling-point of normal hydrogen is $20 \cdot 39_0°$ K. and the triple-point $13 \cdot 95_7°$ K.

When however the $o$-$p$ conversion has proceeded to a final equilibrium the vapour pressure and temperature are connected by the equation (equilibrium hydrogen, $99 \cdot 79$ per cent $p$-$H_2$, $0 \cdot 21$ per cent $o$-$H_2$):

$$\log_{10} p \text{ (mm.)} = 4 \cdot 64392 + 0 \cdot 02093T - 44 \cdot 3450/T$$

It is now standard practice to derive the temperature of a bath of liquid helium ($He^4$) from the vapour pressure–temperature tables accepted at the time. There has been a succession of these proposed temperature scales. That used at present is the 1958 scale proposed by van Dyk, Durieux, Clement and Logan and accepted by the 'Comité International des Poids et Mesures'. It is believed to be superior to previously suggested scales and to be in agreement with the thermodynamic scale to within $\pm 2$ millidegrees. A copy of the table was published in *Physica* in Sept. 1958. On this scale the temperature of the boiling point of helium four is $4 \cdot 215°$ K. and that of the $\lambda$-point $2 \cdot 172°$ K.

The vapour pressure of liquid helium three can be represented by the following formula in the temperature range $1–3 \cdot 3°$ K.

$$\log_{10} p \text{ (mm.)} = \frac{0 \cdot 97796}{T} + 215 \log_{10} T + 0 \cdot 00302T^3 + 1 \cdot 91594$$

in which $T$ is on the 1948 scale with the corrections due to Kistemaker. Below $1°$ K. the vapour pressure of $He^3$ can be represented by:

$$\log_{10} p \text{ (mm.)} = \frac{1 \cdot 10371}{T} + 2 \cdot 3214 \log_{10} T + 2 \cdot 0936 - 0 \cdot 08976T$$
$$+ 0 \cdot 03756T^2 - 0 \cdot 004T^3$$

in the range $0 \cdot 45 - 1 \cdot 0°$ K. The temperatures are given on the $E_{55}$ scale of Clement, Logan and Gaffrey.

The corresponding formulae for the 1958 scale are not yet available.

(d) *Magnetic thermometer*. As mentioned in Chapter I, the temperatures below $1°$ K. produced by the method of adiabatic demagnetization are usually deduced from the measured magnetization of the paramagnetic salt in some small known magnetic field. This provides a very convenient secondary thermometer as the magnetizations are large at these very low temperatures and increase as the temperature falls. The magnetization can be measured either by observing the ballistic throw of a galvanometer in the secondary circuit of a fixed mutual inductance (into which the paramagnetic is inserted) when the current in the primary is reversed or by making the mutual inductance part of a low frequency alternating current bridge. In the latter case it is found that the e.m.f. induced in the secondary has components both in quadrature and in phase with the primary current, corresponding to the complex nature of the susceptibility $\chi = \chi' - i\chi''$. The real part $\chi'$ of the susceptibility is then used to determine the Curie temperature. The imaginary part $\chi''$, which denotes an absorption of energy, is derived from relaxation and hysteresis phenomena. Since the magnetizations are large at these very low temperatures, a correction must be applied to the observed magnetic moment for the demagnetization field. It is also customary to allow for the interior field due to the neighbouring magnetic ions and so express the magnetic moment as a function of the field H acting on the individual dipoles and not of the applied external field $H_{ext}$. Then if $M$ is the magnetic moment of the paramagnetic salt, $V$ its volume and $c$ the Curie constant per cm.$^3$, Curie's law states that $M = HVc/T$. We then have

$$M = \frac{Vc}{T}\left(H_{ext} - N\frac{M}{V} + \tfrac{4}{3}\pi\frac{M}{V}\right)$$

in which $N$ is the demagnetizing coefficient which is a function of the shape of the sample and $\tfrac{4}{3}\pi(M/V)$ is the Lorentz interior field correction. Rearranging, we have

$$M = cVH_{ext}/(T - \Delta)$$

where $\Delta = c(\tfrac{4}{3}\pi - N)$. For a sphere $\Delta = 0$. Temperatures obtained from Curie's law are denoted by $T^*$. Where the above corrections have been applied the temperature may be denoted as $T^*$ (sphere) as the above procedure is equivalent to recalculating from the actual shape of the sample to that of a sphere, so making the work of different observers more directly comparable.

There remains the problem of translating $T^*$ into the absolute temperature $T$. Various procedures have been suggested starting from a known absolute temperature obtainable with liquid helium, say $1°$ K., carrying out cyclical processes involving the lower temperature and calculating the absolute value of the latter by applying Kelvin's definition of absolute temperature.

A method used by Kurti, Lainé and Simon is as follows: The curve of entropy $S$ against $T^*$ for $H = 0$ was first obtained by a series of adiabatic demagnetizations from various initial fields to $H = 0$ starting each time from $1°$ K. (see Fig. 8), the values of $S$ at $1°$ K. being calculated from the Langevin-Brillouin formula (Chapter VI, (18)). Next the curve of $Q$, the amount of heat required to warm the salt from $T^*$ to the initial temperature ($1°$ K.) as a function of $T^*$ was determined by applying a constant source of heat and observing $T^*$ as a function of the time of heating. The heating was obtained by the absorption in the paramagnetic salt of $\gamma$-rays from a radioactive source placed outside the cryostat. This method of heating has several advantages: (i) the heating is uniform over the whole sample avoiding difficulties due to the very bad heat conduction through a powdered substance at very low temperatures which makes normal electrical heating almost impossible; (ii) it is easily varied by varying the distance between the radioactive source and the powdered salt; (iii) it supplies conveniently small amounts of heat of the order of 100–1000 erg/min. The absolute amount of heat supplied has, however, to be determined by a calibration of the source. This was done by using the known specific heat of the powder at $1°$ K. and assuming that the Curie scale and the absolute scale coincide at this temperature.

The absolute temperature $T$ corresponding to $T^*$ can then be calculated from

$$T = \frac{\Delta Q}{\Delta S} = \frac{(\partial Q/\partial T^*)_{H=0}}{(\partial S/\partial T^*)_{H=0}}$$

The Curie temperature derived as mentioned above is shown in Fig. 9 as a function of the absolute temperature for the case of iron ammonium alum. The two scales do not differ greatly down to 0·3° K. but large differences occur below this temperature. In the neighbourhood of 0·04° K., where the sudden drop in the curve occurs, the susceptibility shows a sharp maximum and hysteresis phenomena begin to appear as described later in Chapter VI.

In the corresponding case of chromium potassium alum de Klerk, Steenland and Gorter found even greater differences between the $T^*$ and $T$ scales. Thus while $T^* = 0·06°$ corresponded to $T = 0·035°$ K., the lowest temperature measured, $T^* = 0·033°$ was equivalent to $T = 0·0039°$ K.

Other measurable quantities besides $\chi'$ can be used to determine very low temperatures. Thus de Klerk, Steenland and Gorter have used $\chi''$, the observed remanence and the area of the hysteresis loop of chromium potassium alum. By applying an alternating magnetic field heat is supplied at the rate given by

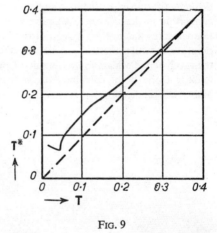

FIG. 9

$$\frac{dQ}{dt} = \tfrac{1}{2} H_0^2 \omega \chi''$$

and the absolute temperature can again be obtained from $\Delta Q = T \Delta S$. This method of heating possesses the advantage that the heat is generated directly in the spin system and not by absorption in the atomic nuclei and later transmission to the spin system as in the $\gamma$-ray method. It also tends to reduce temperature differences in the sample as the coldest parts receive the most heat in the $\chi''$ method. Again, if the remanence is determined as a function of $S$ and the change of remanence for a known $\Delta Q$ the temperature can be determined. The area of the hysteresis loop can also be used to determine $\Delta Q$. All three methods give satisfactory agreement with the temperatures derived from $\chi'$ but are more suitable for temperatures near the Curie point (see Chapter VI), where the $\chi'$ thermometer becomes less reliable or impossible.

*Nuclear cooling.* There is now the problem of measuring the temperatures in the microdegree region obtained by Kurti and his co-workers by means of nuclear cooling. These temperatures are measured by determining the nuclear susceptibility by a ballistic method and assuming that this susceptibility obeys Curie's law. This is difficult on account of the smallness of the temperature-dependent paramagnetic susceptibility due to the nuclear spins in comparison with the corresponding electronic spin susceptibilities involved in the demagnetization experiments at higher temperatures. The problem of converting nuclear Curie temperatures to absolute thermodynamic temperatures has not yet arisen. However, an estimate of the temperature at which the Curie scale will differ considerably from the thermodynamic scale can be obtained from the temperature of the nuclear Curie point calculated from the theory of Fröhlich and Nabarro. Hobden and Kurti estimate this to be $1 \cdot 9 \times 10^{-7}$ ° K.

## CHAPTER III

# Liquid and Solid Helium

The determination of the physical properties of liquid and solid helium will serve well as a first illustration of physical research at very low temperatures. The existence of two stable isotopes of helium, $He^4$ and $He^3$, provides a unique opportunity to determine the very contrasting properties of isotopes of odd and even mass. Both liquid $He^4$ and liquid $He^3$ have proved very interesting as they possess properties not found in any other substance. Furthermore, each of these substances exists as a liquid under its saturated vapour pressure right down to $0°$ K. All other substances form crystalline solids at triple points well above $10°$ K.

**Liquid Helium Four**
Helium ($He^4$), the last of the so-called permanent gases to be liquefied, was first obtained in the liquid state by Kamerlingh Onnes in 1908. It is a colourless, mobile, very volatile liquid boiling at $4·215°$ K. under a pressure of 1 atm. As mentioned in Chapter I, helium remains a mobile liquid even when its vapour pressure is reduced to $0·0036$ mm. Hg ($T = 0·726°$ K.). This observation and later evidence obtained when liquid $He^4$ was cooled to about $0·01°$ K. by means of a paramagnetic salt indicates that $He^4$ does not possess a triple point at which vapour, liquid and solid are in equilibrium. This conclusion is confirmed by the shape of the melting curve of solid helium, first obtained by Keesom.

The first indication, apart from the absence of a triple point, that liquid $He^4$ possesses unusual properties was obtained by Kamerlingh Onnes and Boks who found that the density-temperature curve (Fig. 10, curve 1) shows a marked discontinuity in slope at $2·172°$ K. As Atkins and Edwards have shown the coefficient of expansion is negative below this temperature down to $1·15°$ K. where it changes sign and at still lower temperatures tends again to zero at $0°$ K. The dielectric constant shows a very similar variation with temperature (Fig. 10, curve 2).

The specific heat of liquid $He^4$ has been measured with the results shown in Fig. 11 (Keesom and Keesom). $C_s$ (the specific heat of the liquid in equilibrium with its saturated vapour) shows a very high maximum of at least 3·0 cal./gm. deg. at 2·172° K. Between 0·6° K. and 1·4° K. the specific heat is given by $C = 0.024T^{6.2}$ cal./gm. deg. and below 0·6° K. by $C = 0.00487T^3$ cal./gm. deg. It has been established that the curve of Fig. 11 represents the true specific heat and is not the result of a latent heat evolved in the neighbourhood of

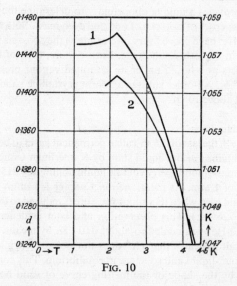

Fig. 10

2·172° K. The shape of the curve is similar to that of the specific heat of ferromagnetics near the Curie point, where the ferromagnetism disappears, and of certain alloys such as $\beta$-brass, where an ordered arrangement of the Cu and Zn atoms changes to a disordered arrangement. The conclusion is that liquid $He^4$ is in a more ordered state below 2·172° K. than it is above this temperature. The ordering, however, appears to occur in momentum space rather than in co-ordinate space.

The latent heat of vaporization of liquid $He^4$ has been determined by Dana and Kamerlingh Onnes and Berman and Poulter. The results of the former authors are shown in Fig. 12, together with the curve calculated from the second latent heat equation

$$dL/dT - L/T = C'_s - C''_s$$

($L =$ latent heat, $C'_s$ and $C''_s$ specific heats of saturated vapour and saturated liquid respectively). The agreement is good and shows that there is no sudden jump in the value of $L$ at $2 \cdot 172°$ K. as concluded from the specific heat observations. The extreme volatility of liquid He$^4$ and the consequent necessity of special precautions against

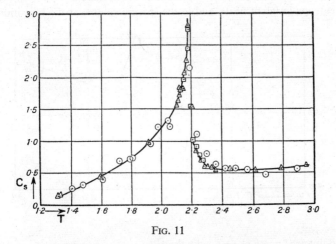

FIG. 11

heat entry if the liquid is to be preserved for any length of time are clearly brought out by the very small value of $L$, about 5·5 cal./gm. between 1·5° K. and 3·0° K. (Compare the value 110 cal./gm. for hydrogen at 20° K. and 536 cal./gm. for water at 373° K.)

These properties led Keesom and Wolfke to suggest that at 2·172° K. (under its saturated vapour pressure) helium changes from one liquid phase into another liquid phase. These two phases are referred to as liquid He I and liquid He II and the transition point as the λ-point. At higher pressures the temperature of the λ-point varies with pressure as shown in the lower curve of Fig. 13. This curve, the λ-curve, meets the melting curve (see p. 45) at 29·64 atm. and 1·764° K. (Swenson). This point is thus a triple point in the $p$. $T$ diagram and the curves meeting in it separate regions in which solid He, liquid He I and liquid He II exist. The phenomenon of the maximum density of liquid He⁴ persists all along the λ-curve, becoming more pronounced as the 'triple point' is approached.

The existence of the λ-transition at which there is no latent heat and of other transitions of a similar nature in superconductors, in ferromagnetics and in certain ammonium salts, led Ehrenfest to postulate the occurrence of *second-order transitions*. Transitions such as solid ↔ liquid, crystal α ↔ crystal β, at which there is a jump in the entropy (a latent heat), and in the specific volume at the transition

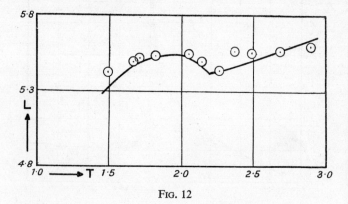

Fig. 12

point are known as *first-order transitions* as the *first* derivative of the Gibbs function, $G = U - TS + pV$ shows a *discontinuity* at the transition point. In a *second-order transition*, the Gibbs function and its first derivative are continuous at the transition point but the *second derivative* is *discontinuous*. Consequently, there is a jump of the specific heat and of the coefficient of expansion. For second-order transitions Ehrenfest deduced the following equations:

$$\left(\frac{dp}{dT}\right)_\lambda = \frac{C_{p,\mathrm{II}} - C_{p,\mathrm{I}}}{TV(\alpha_{\mathrm{II}} - \alpha_{\mathrm{I}})}; \quad \left(\frac{dp}{dT}\right)_\lambda = \frac{\alpha_{\mathrm{II}} - \alpha_{\mathrm{I}}}{K_{T,\mathrm{II}} - K_{T,\mathrm{I}}}$$

where $C_{p,\mathrm{I}}$ and $C_{p,\mathrm{II}}$ are the specific heats at constant pressure of the two phases, $\alpha_{\mathrm{I}}$, $\alpha_{\mathrm{II}}$ the coefficients of expansion and $K_{T,\mathrm{I}}$, $K_{T,\mathrm{II}}$ the isothermal compressibilities. The first of these relations is approximately true for the λ-transition in liquid He$^4$ but owing to the very rapid variation of the specific heat near the λ-point it is difficult to make a more precise statement. It is now believed that the λ-transition is of a more complicated nature than the second-order transition envisaged by Ehrenfest. The only transition definitely known to be of the second order is that of superconductivity to normal conductivity in the absence of a magnetic field (see Chapter V).

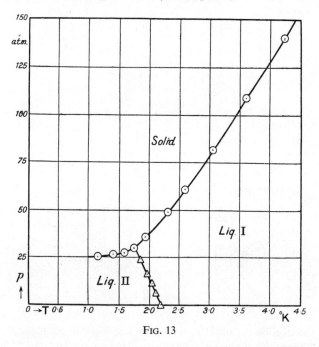

Fig. 13

The most remarkable properties of liquid helium II are, however, exhibited not when it is stationary but when a flow is associated with it. Thus when a small beaker is immersed in liquid helium II so that the level of the liquid inside the beaker is initially lower than that of the liquid outside (Fig. 14), the difference in level is seen gradually to decrease until finally the helium stands at exactly the same height inside and outside the beaker. Similarly, if the level of the liquid in the beaker is initially higher than that of the liquid outside, the reverse process occurs. If the beaker is lifted out of the liquid helium II as in Fig. 14(*b*), the liquid is seen to fall from the bottom of the beaker in small drops until the latter is empty. These transfer phenomena were first studied by Daunt and Mendelssohn. It was shown that a film of liquid creeps over the walls of the beaker and transfers helium towards the lower liquid level. The rate of transfer is proportional to the length

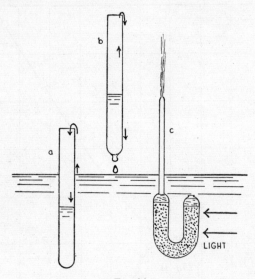

Fig. 14

of the smallest perimeter of the beaker above the upper liquid level and, except for the first few millimetres from the rim and the last few millimetres before equalization of the levels, is independent of the difference in height of the two liquid levels. It is, therefore not a siphon process as exhibited by viscous liquids. The rate depends on the temperature, rising in the case of a Pyrex glass beaker from zero at the $\lambda$-point to about $8\cdot5 \times 10^{-5}$ cm.$^3$/cm. sec. at $1\cdot0°$ K. Measurements have shown that the transfer rate varies very little between $1\cdot5°$ K. and $1\cdot0°$ K., and on current views on the nature of the transfer phenomenon practically no further variation should occur down to 0° K. Nevertheless, several observers have recorded increases of the transfer rate below 1° K. (an increase of 25 per cent as the temperature falls to 0·3° K.). As the low temperature has in every case been obtained by adiabatic demagnetization and as the warming times have been relatively short, the experiments have not yet been carried out under adequately isothermal conditions and the results must be accepted with caution.

The early observations of transfer rate particularly on metals and plastics were very discordant until Mendelssohn and Bowers discovered that a thin layer of solid condensed on the surface very greatly increases the observed transfer rate. The detailed work of Smith and Boorse has established what is now known about the transfer rate on metals but it cannot yet be said that it is definitely known whether the rate is independent of the chemical nature of the substrate. The observed rate is influenced by the microstructure of the surface and this is not known sufficiently well.

All solid surfaces in contact with liquid helium II are covered by this very mobile film. If there is an appreciable heat input into the solid wall the film evaporates at the place where the temperature is equal to the λ-temperature. If the vapour so produced can condense back in the liquid helium II this process results in a very considerable heat leak into the bath. Daunt and Mendelssohn made the first determination of the thickness of the film, giving an average value of $3·5 \times 10^{-6}$ cm. The problem of the determination of the film thickness under adequately isothermal conditions is a difficult one and only recently have consistent values of thickness been obtained. The most recent measurements of Grimes and Jackson and of Dillinger and his co-workers have shown that the thickness $d$ of the helium II film is nearly equal to that calculated from $d = k/H^{1/3}$, where $k$ varies slightly with temperature and $H$ is the height of the point of observation about the liquid level. The following values are typical: $T = 2·05°$ K., $d = 3·22 \times 10^{-6}$ cm.; $T = 1·83°$ K., $d = 3·10 \times 10^{-6}$ cm.; $T = 1·63°$ K., $d = 3·08 \times 10^{-6}$ cm. If the film is held on to the substrate by van der Waals forces of attraction the thickness will be given by the expression quoted above with $k$ independent of the temperature (Schiff, Frenkel). A more complete theory by Franchetti shows the Gibbs function of the Helium II in the film must contain terms which are a consequence of the thinness of the film and which add a term $c/H^{1/2}$ to the expression for $d$, where $c$ is a function of the temperature. Theoretically a film should exist above the $\lambda$-point but as a helium I film will not have the great mobility of the helium II film the former is easily evaporated by any stray heat input. The existence of a film in the helium I region has recently been proved by Grimes and Jackson but its thickness is greatly dependent on the experimental conditions.

According to measurements by Bowers and by Grenier the thermal conductivity of liquid helium I varies almost linearly from $7 \times 10^{-5}$ cal./deg. cm. sec. at $4 \cdot 0°$ K. to $3 \times 10^{-5}$ at $2 \cdot 2°$ K., when measured at the saturated vapour pressure. These values are closely similar to the thermal conductivity of helium gas at room temperature and agree roughly with the expression derived from the kinetic theory, $K = $ const. $\times \eta C_v$, where $K = $ thermal conductivity, $\eta = $ viscosity and $C_v = $ specific heat at constant volume. The rate of transport of heat through liquid helium II has been investigated by a number of workers and has proved to be very abnormal. Liquid helium II, enclosed in a fine capillary tube, does not possess a definite thermal conductivity at any specified temperature since the apparent conductivity varies with the temperature gradient, or, what is an equivalent statement, with the heat input, increasing as the heat input decreases. The apparent conductivity shows a maximum near $1 \cdot 9°$ K. which shifts to higher temperatures as the heat input is decreased. For the smallest heat input used by Keesom and Saris this maximum of the apparent conductivity reached the astonishing figure of 1900 cal./deg. cm. sec., about $3 \times 10^7$ times greater than that of liquid helium I at a temperature 1 deg. higher and 2000 times that of copper at room temperature.

It is obvious that such an anomalous heat transport cannot be produced by the normal process of thermal conduction such as occurs in liquid helium I, but is due rather to an actual transport of mass along the capillary compensated by some kind of return flow since there is no total movement of liquid from the hot end to the cold end. The existence of such a flow† has been demonstrated convincingly by Kapitza. Again, the presence of a maximum effect near $1 \cdot 9°$ K. can

† It is not to be confused with ordinary convection in a liquid, since the flow in question is not produced by the combined effect of gravity and variations in density.

be explained as the rate of transport of heat is proportional to the heat content of the flowing liquid and its velocity, provided this velocity decreases to zero at the λ-point as the temperature rises. It has also been shown by Kurti and Simon that the anomalously high thermal conductivity of liquid helium II disappears at very low temperatures, the observed values being $2 \cdot 2 \times 10^{-3}$ cal./deg. cm. sec. at $0 \cdot 5°$ K. and $0 \cdot 2 \times 10^{-3}$ at $0 \cdot 2°$ K.

Another remarkable property of liquid helium II was discovered by Allen and Jones with the apparatus shown in Fig. 14(c). It was designed to investigate the viscosity of the liquid by measuring the rate of flow through the tightly packed emery powder filling the lower part of the tube. When the apparatus was immersed in liquid helium II to the depth shown and light from a small lamp was shone on the emery powder, a jet of liquid helium was projected out of the upper open end of the tube to a height of several centimetres, as long as the emery powder was illuminated. This fountain effect results from the direct transformation of the heat energy absorbed by the emery powder into kinetic energy of the liquid helium II. Later investigations showed that the fountain effect is a particular case of the general statement that whenever a temperature gradient is established in liquid helium II a pressure gradient is produced. A thermodynamical treatment of the problem by H. London showed that the effect is governed by the general formula $dp/dT = \rho S$, where $\rho$ is the density of liquid helium and $S$ its entropy. Kapitza and other workers later established the quantitative relations of the phenomenon by accurate measurements of the rate at which liquid helium II enters a bulb through a narrow channel $(1 - 30 \times 10^{-5}$ cm.) when heat is generated electrically at a known rate in the bulb. For these very narrow channels and for low heat inputs the phenomena were found to be thermodynamically reversible and there was no observable temperature difference between the helium inside the bulb and that outside. The observations could be interpreted by supposing that the liquid helium flowing into the bulb did not convey entropy, so that to maintain the temperature of the liquid in the bulb constant while 1 gm. of liquid helium enters the bulb an amount of heat $Q$ had to be supplied equal to $ST$, where $S$ is the entropy per gm. of liquid helium II at temperature $T$.

The converse of the fountain effect (the mechano-caloric effect) was

4

discovered by Daunt and Mendelssohn who showed that if liquid helium II is forced through a very narrow channel the emerging helium has a lower temperature (see p. 26).

The viscosity of liquid helium I decreases from 33 micropoise at $5 \cdot 0°$ K. to 30 $\mu$P at $2 \cdot 7°$ K. It then decreases more rapidly reaching 23 $\mu$P just above the $\lambda$-point. The slow decrease with falling temperature shows that liquid helium I behaves more like a gas in this respect than like other liquids, as may be expected from its low density. When the viscosity is measured at pressures higher than the saturated vapour pressure, the behaviour gradually changes to that of other liquids, the viscosity ultimately (at densities higher than $0 \cdot 17$ gm./cm.³) falling with increase in temperature.

The phenomena of heat transport in liquid helium II and the fountain effect suggest that the viscosity of liquid helium II is very small. It has proved to be both small and highly anomalous.

The viscosity of liquid helium II has been investigated by the measurement of (1) the damping of the oscillations of a disc immersed in the liquid, (2) the rate of flow through capillary tubes and (3) the rate of flow through very narrow channels (of the order of $5 \times 10^{-5}$ cm.) such as a tube filled with many fine wires or the gap between two optically flat discs. The oscillating disc method measures the product of the density and the viscosity of the liquid, $\rho\eta$. The values of $\eta$ obtained by using for $\rho$ the observed density of the liquid fit well on to the values for liquid helium I quoted above. The viscosity then falls rapidly below the $\lambda$-point reaching a value of about $1 \times 10^{-6}$ poise at $1 \cdot 3°$ K. As mentioned later this interpretation of the observations is not the correct one and the temperature variation of the viscosity at the lowest temperatures is different.

Using the third method with optically flat discs, with a separation of $0 \cdot 5$ $\mu$, Kapitza observed that liquid helium II flowed so rapidly through this very narrow gap under a pressure head of a few centimetres of liquid that accurate measurements were hardly possible. Furthermore, the rate of flow was apparently independent of the pressure head. It was calculated that the maximum value which the viscosity of liquid helium II could have had under these conditions was $10^{-3}$ $\mu$P. Allen and Reekie using wire-filled tubes also observed a flow independent of pressure head and varying with temperature in the same way as film flow. The observations made it clear that liquid helium II flows through *sufficiently narrow* channels with a *complete absence* of viscous drag; it shows *superfluidity*.

The flow through fairly wide capillary tubes exhibits a complicated situation which is difficult to interpret. Velocities of flow show different variations with pressure head for the various diameters of tube and the whole picture varies with the temperature. In some cases the flow can be separated into a superfluid flow independent of the pressure head and a Poiseuille flow of normal fluid proportional to the pressure head and leading to a value of $\eta$ agreeing with the oscillating disc value. In general, however, the situation is much more complicated and there may be turbulence both in the superfluid and in the normal fluid. The dissipation experienced by the superfluid at higher velocities is now attributed to the production of a tangle of vortex lines in the superfluid. The whole is further complicated by the existence of the fountain effect as a result of which temperature differences may be set up and exactly isothermal flow is difficult to realize. These properties of liquid helium II can be described by a two-fluid model proposed initially by Tisza on the basis of the properties of a Bose-Einstein fluid and extended later by various workers, particularly by Landau from his quantum hydrodynamics. The liquid behaves as if it consists of two interpenetrating fluids, one of which, the *normal fluid*, has a density $\rho_n$ and properties entirely similar to those of liquid helium I. The other fluid is the *superfluid* of density $\rho_s$ and zero, or vanishingly small, viscosity. The observed density of liquid helium II is then given by

$$\rho = \rho_s + \rho_n$$

The relative proportions of the two fluids varies with the temperature so that $\rho_s/\rho = 1$ at $0°$ K. and 0 at the $\lambda$-point while $\rho_n/\rho = 0$ at $0°$ K. and 1 at the $\lambda$-point is indicated in Fig. 15. Each component moves with its own velocity so that the momentum per unit mass is given by

$$\rho_s v_s + \rho_n v_n$$

To account for the results of experiments on the thermal conductivity and those of Kapitza and others on the flow of liquid helium II induced by heat input the entropy of the superfluid is taken as zero or vanishingly small so that the whole of the entropy of liquid helium II is carried by the normal component. The shape of the specific heat curve requires that the energy levels of the superfluid shall be separated from the lowest level of the normal fluid. The small rise in the specific heat on the high temperature side of the $\lambda$-point may be due to the presence of inclusions of liquid helium II in the liquid helium I as a result of fluctuations near the $\lambda$-point. Pippard has pointed out that inclusions of the required size can be expected on the theory of fluctuations at even half a degree above the $\lambda$-point. The marked drop in the viscosity of liquid helium I just above the $\lambda$-point observed by Bowers and Mendelssohn may be due to the same cause.

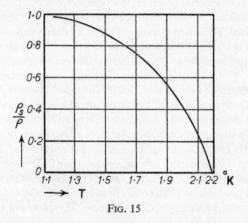

FIG. 15

In the determination of the viscosity of liquid helium II by the oscillating disc the damping of the oscillations is caused by the normal fluid. The superfluid slips past the moving disc without any interaction. Consequently the normal fluid density $\rho_n$ should be used in the calculation of the viscosity which will then be the viscosity of the normal fluid. Then $\eta_n$ falls from 20·5 $\mu$P at 2·17° K. to 11·25 $\mu$P at 1·69° K. and rises to 20·4 $\mu$P at 1·32° K. It continues to rise rapidly as the temperature falls below 1·0° K. (about 65 $\mu$P at 0·7° K.).

In flow through wide tubes the normal fluid controls the flow but in very narrow channels the flow at sufficiently small velocities is almost exclusively that of the superfluid to which the narrow channel offers no resistance. Film flow at sub-critical velocities is an example of pure superfluid flow.

The proportion of normal fluid present at any temperature below the $\lambda$-point has been determined by Andronikashvili. He measured the moment of inertia of a cylinder containing a stack of circular discs separated by about 0·1 mm. from each other when it oscillated about the cylinder axis in liquid helium. Above the $\lambda$-point the liquid in the narrow gap between the discs was carried round with the latter and so contributed to the moment of inertia of the system. Below the $\lambda$-point only the normal fluid took part in the oscillation, the superfluid remaining stationary. Thus the observed moment of inertia decreased as the temperature was lowered below the $\lambda$-point and the ratio $\rho_n/\rho$ could be deduced. The corresponding values of $\rho_s/\rho$ are plotted against the temperature in Fig. 15.

The two-fluid model possesses another interesting property. A wave motion, propagated in liquid helium II, can be imagined in which the superfluid and normal fluid contained in any small element of volume oscillate together in phase. This represents a periodic change in density at constant temperature and corresponds to the propagation of a sound wave. It is also possible to imagine a wave motion in which the superfluid and normal fluid oscillate in antiphase causing a periodic variation of the ratio of $\rho_s$ to $\rho_n$. This corresponds to an oscillation of the temperature. The existence of this thermal wave or 'second sound' as it was called by Landau was predicted by Tisza and by Landau. By writing down the differential equations for the conservation of mass, momentum and entropy on the two-fluid model and the equation for the force acting on the superfluid alone, one can derive two equations, the solutions of which are (1) a periodic propagation of differences in pressure with a velocity $u_1^2 = (\partial p/\partial \rho)_s$ ('first sound') and (2) a periodic propagation of changes in entropy (or of temperature) with velocity $u_2^2 = \rho_s T S^2/\rho_n C$ where $C$ is the specific heat ('second sound').

Inserting the known values of the compressibility in the equation for $u_1$ gives velocities which agree well with those determined directly. Thus $u_1$ measured at the saturated vapour pressure, varies from 180 m./sec. at 4·2° K. to 220 m./sec. near the $\lambda$-point, to 235 m./sec. at 1·0° K. and extrapolating to 239 m./sec. at 0° K. The attenuation of first sound shows a very striking variation with temperature at constant frequency. In the liquid helium I region the attenuation coefficient $\alpha$ falls steadily with decreasing temperature in a way explicable by the classical theory of the effects of viscosity and thermal conductivity on the wave amplitude. Then there is a very sharp peak in the neighbourhood of the $\lambda$-point associated with the relaxation processes occurring in a second-order transition. At $2 \cdot 0°$ K. $\alpha$ has again fallen to a low value; it then rises to a broader maximum at about $1 \cdot 0°$ K. and then falls to zero at $0°$ K. The value of $\alpha$ below $2 \cdot 0°$ K. has been shown to be associated with the various relaxation times of the collision processes in the excitations in liquid helium II (the phonons and rotons, see p. 66).†

The velocity of second sound, $u_2$, rises from 0 at the $\lambda$-point to 20 m./sec. at $1 \cdot 8°$ K., shows a very shallow minimum near $1 \cdot 0°$ K. and rises to at least 190 m./sec. at $0°$ K. According to Landau the expected value of $u_2$ at $0°$ K. is 137 m./sec. $(= u_1/\sqrt{3})$. Actually there is a small plateau in the curve at this velocity but the measured values of $u_2$ appear to be approaching 239 m./sec. $(= u_1)$ at $0°$ K. The discrepancy is probably caused by the intervention of mean-free path effects at the lowest temperatures. The attenuation of second sound falls from its value at the $\lambda$-point to a minimum at $2 \cdot 0°$ K. and then rises steadily as the temperature falls. It can be explained in terms of the collision processes of the phonons and rotons.

Second sound was first detected by Peshkov by observing the stationary waves set up in a resonant column of liquid helium II by a periodically heated wire grid immersed in the liquid. Other workers have studied the propagation of pulses of second sound, and Pellam has detected second sound by means of a Rayleigh disc, the torque on which is proportional to the mechanical energy associated with the wave $(\rho_n v_n^2 + \rho_s v_s^2)$.

The simple two-fluid picture described above is really valid only for small velocities of flow, there being a critical velocity, associated with each type of experiment, below which the superfluid flow is resistanceless. For higher velocities of flow and for larger amplitudes of oscillation of the discs there is evidence of a dissipation term proportional to $(v_s - v_n)^3$ (Gorter and Mellink).

The simplest form of the hydrodynamical equations for the two-

† If a relaxation process occurs with a relaxation time $\tau$ and if the latter is a rapidly varying function of the temperature, there will be a very large attenuation of a wave at the temperature for which $\tau$ is equal to the periodic time of the sound wave.

fluid model lead to the conclusion that flow of the superfluid must be irrotational (curl$v_s = 0$) when $v_s$ is smaller than the critical velocity relevant to the experimental conditions. This prediction fits well with cases where a definite critical velocity is experimentally observable. However, its application to rotating liquid helium II has revealed a new situation. For a singly connected sample such as liquid helium II in a cylindrical vessel rotating uniformly about its axis, the condition curl$v_s = 0$ implies $v_s = 0$ and so the superfluid is expected to remain stationary while the normal fluid rotates with the beaker. Now the free surface of a liquid rotating in a cylindrical vessel has a cross-section parallel to the axis of rotation which is a parabola $y = \omega^2 x^2/2g$, where $\omega$ is the angular velocity, $y$ is the height of the surface at a distance $x$ from the axis. In helium II if only the normal component rotates the surface would be $y = \rho_n \omega^2 x^2/2\rho g$. Osborne, however, found that when the peripheral speed was 35–70 cm./sec., the shape of the surface corresponded to the rotation of the whole liquid. Andronikashvili and Kaverkin later showed that this is also the case down to a speed as low as 4 cm./sec. Hall measured the torque required to accelerate a cylindrical vessel of liquid helium II to a constant angular velocity. Again, the conclusion was reached that both normal and superfluid were rotating.

In Andronikashvili's experiment with the oscillating discs, on the other hand, only the normal fluid took part in the motion. In Hall's experiment the liquid helium II was accelerated for about 1 min. before the velocity became constant whereas the period of oscillation of the discs was about 1 sec. It thus appears that the whole liquid can be brought into rotation provided the time is long enough and so some new feature must be present in the rotating helium II.

Feynman has substituted the less restrictive condition

$$\oint v_s dl = nh/m$$

where $n$ is an integer and $m$ is the mass of the helium atom, for the condition curl$v_s = 0$. Then in Osborne's experiment curl$v_s = 0$ is satisfied everywhere except in the immediate neighbourhood of a number of quantized line vortices, parallel to the axis of rotation and about each of which there is a circulation of the magnitude $nh/m$. The free surface will then be the paraboloid corresponding to rotation of the whole liquid on which is superposed a number of shallow

depressions where the line vortices meet the free surface. It is estimated that the vortices would be spaced about $2 \times 10^{-4}$ cm. apart in
Osborne's experiment ($\omega =$ about 100 radians per sec.) and that the
depression of the surface would be somewhere between $10 \mu$ and $10$ Å.
The presence of the vortices would therefore have not been detected
in this experiment.

Evidence for the existence of the line vortices and for the quantiz-
ation of the circulation has been obtained by Vinen. A cylindrical
vessel containing liquid He II has a fine wire stretched along its axis.
If the system is set in rotation it will be expected that there will be a
circulation of one or more quanta about the axial wire. In the presence
of such a circulation the transverse vibrations of the wire will be re-
solved into two circularly polarized vibrations with opposite directions
of rotation whose frequencies differ by an amount $\rho_s K / 2\pi w$, where
$K$ is the circulation and $w$ the mass per unit length of the wire. These
vibrations are detected by observing the voltage generated between
the ends of the wire due to the presence of a constant magnetic field.

The apparatus was rotated at a temperature above the $\lambda$-point and
then slowly cooled to $1 \cdot 3°$ K. and maintained at that temperature.
The observed circulation about the wire in the rotating helium II was
never an exact multiple of $h/m$. If, however, the vessel was stopped, the
circulation decreased and after about 20 min. reached the value $h/m$
and remained constant within 2 per cent for the duration of the
experiment (about a further 100 min.).

Uniformly rotating liquid helium II should then contain a uniformly spaced array of vortex lines in the superfluid parallel to the
axis of rotation. The number of lines per unit area normal to the axis
would be $2\omega/K$; for $\omega = 1$ radian per sec. and $K = h/m$ the lines would
be spaced about $0 \cdot 2$ mm. apart. By measuring the attenuation of
second sound in uniformly rotating helium II, Hall and Vinen have
obtained experimental results entirely in accord with this picture of
the superfluid. The extra attenuation is caused by the collision of the
excitations in helium II (phonons and rotons) with the vortex lines
and indicates that there is a force of mutual friction between superfluid and normal fluid per unit volume of the latter which is given by

$$F_{sn} = B \frac{\rho_s \rho_n}{\rho} \omega (v_s - v_n)$$

This is a linear dissipative force due to a uniformly spaced array of vortex lines. Further studies have, however, shown that the existence of non-linear dissipative forces such as the Gorter-Mellink force proportional to $(v_s - v_n)^3$ is a consequence of turbulence in the superfluid due to an irregularly spaced array or tangle of vortex lines.

## Solid Helium Four

Solid $He^4$ was first produced by Keesom in 1926 by the combined effects of high pressure and low temperature on the liquid. His apparatus is shown diagrammatically in Fig. 16. With the stop-cocks $K_2$ and $K_4$ shut and stop-cock $K_1$ open, gaseous helium was compressed into the narrow nickel-silver tube $B_1$ and the brass capillary $B_2$. The latter was immersed in liquid helium boiling at some known pressure. The gas liquefied and collected in $B_2$. To determine whether the helium solidified on further increase of pressure, $K_4$ and $K_1$ were shut and $K_2$ opened. If now the helium had solidified the capillary $B_2$ would be blocked and on releasing the pressure by opening $K_2$ a difference of pressure would be registered on the differential manometer D. In this way it was found that at 4·0° K. the capillary was blocked when the pressure, as read on the gauge $P_1$ was 128 kg./cm.$^2$ and was open when the pressure was 126 kg./cm.$^2$. Proceeding in this way, it was possible to determine the melting curve of $He^4$. The results are shown in the upper curve of Fig. 13. It will be seen that the melting pressure tends to become independent of the temperature at the lowest temperatures. It appears that, even in the immediate neighbourhood of 0° K., solid $He^4$ cannot exist at any pressure less than about 25 atm. Simon and his co-workers, using the same general method, have extended the observations to 7270 atm. at which the solid ↔ fluid transition occurs at 50° K., a temperature very much higher than the liquid–gas critical temperature (5·2° K.). Assuming that no solid–fluid critical point occurs within the range and extrapolating the present data it may be estimated that $He^4$ would be solid at room temperature under a pressure of about 100,000 atm. The melting curve has since been studied in more detail by Swenson and by Mills and Grilly.

After having shown that the pressures required to solidify $He^4$ below 2° K. are not excessively high, Keesom repeated the observations with a thick-walled glass bulb F in order to render the solid $He^4$

visible. The bulb was provided with a stirrer in the shape of a small piece of soft iron H which could be moved up and down by means of a magnetized iron ring immersed in the helium bath. At a pressure to be expected from Fig. 13, the stirrer was seen to stick. No line of demarcation between the liquid and the solid was, however, visible. He$^4$ thus solidifies to a homogeneous transparent mass, the refractive index and density of which do not differ much from those of the liquid at the same pressure and temperature. The density determined later was found to be 0·17 gm./cm.$^3$ at 1·0° K. and 0·22 gm./cm.$^3$ at 4·0° K. along the melting curve. These low densities are an indication of the importance of the large zero-point energy of He$^4$ in determining the density and structure of the solid. X-ray investigations by Keesom and Taconis have shown that He$^4$ crystallizes in a close-packed hexagonal structure with a distance of 3·75 Å between the nearest neighbours at 1·45° K. As the diameter of the helium atom is about 2·4 Å, this leaves ample 'room' for the quite considerable amplitude of the zero-point vibrations. Later work by Dugdale and Simon on the entropy of solid He$^4$ has indicated that a first-order phase transition with a latent heat of 0·08 cal./mole occurs in the solid at higher densities (at about 15° K. and a molar volume of about 12 cm.$^3$). The transition is probably to a cubic structure similar to that of the other inert gases.

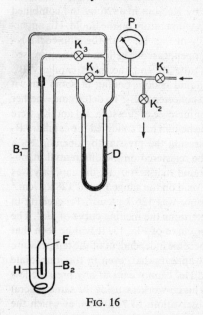

FIG. 16

From the Clausius-Clapeyron equation

$$dp/dT = (S_1 - S_2)/(v_1 - v_2)$$

whose $S_1$, $S_2$ are the entropies per gm., and $v_1$, $v_2$ the specific volumes of the liquid and solid respectively and the fact that $dp/dT$ tends to zero at $0°$ K. for the melting curve of solid $He^4$, it may be deduced that the difference in entropy of solid and liquid $He^4$ tends similarly to zero† in accordance with the Third Law of Thermodynamics. This indicates that at very low temperatures liquid He II possesses almost the same degree of order as solid $He^4$, although the former is the most mobile liquid known and the latter is a crystalline solid. Though the degree of order is the same the kind of order is different, that of liquid He II being in the momenta, that of solid $He^4$ in the spatial positions of the helium atoms. Furthermore, the smallness of the entropy difference even up to the λ-curve shows that the latent heat of melting (solid $He^4 \leftrightarrow$ liq. He II) is much smaller than that of the transition solid $\leftrightarrow$ liquid in other substances. Simon and Swenson have drawn attention to an interesting feature of the melting of solid helium. Since $\Delta S$ is practically zero for any temperature below $1°$ K., the latent heat of melting is also zero. It is, therefore, not possible to melt solid $He^4$ isothermally by supplying heat; instead one must reduce the pressure.

Solid $He^4$ is a particularly interesting substance to study. It is possible to examine its properties at 'reduced' values of the temperature and pressure covering a much greater range than with any other substance. Again, on account of the great compressibility of solid $He^4$ (about $1.5 \times 10^{-3}$ atm. $^{-1}$ at $3.7°$ K. and 115 atm.) it is possible to study the variation of its properties with temperature at a series of appreciably different constant densities. Thus specific heats have been measured down to about $0.25°$ K., leading to values of the Debye $\theta$‡ of about 25 to 35, according to the density. These low values of $\theta_D$ are evidence of the weakness of the forces between the atoms of helium in the crystal lattice. Thermal conductivities have also been measured at various densities. They each show a sharp maximum (for example, about $0.12$ watt/cm. deg. at about $0.85°$ K. for a density of $0.194$ gm./cm.³) of which the value rises and the position shifts to higher temperatures as the density increases. The values found lead to the suggestion of using solid helium as a contact medium below $0.5°$ K.

† The experimental evidence shows that the difference in specific volumes remains finite as the temperature falls.

‡ See Chapter IV.

in adiabatic demagnetization as the thermal conductivity of solid $He^4$ is greater than that of liquid $He^4$ at these very low temperatures.

## Liquid and Solid Helium Three

Helium gas extracted from the air contains about one part in a million of the lighter isotope $He^3$. It is also present to a smaller extent in helium obtained from oil wells. Much work has been done on concentrating the lighter isotope and in studying the properties of mixtures of $He^3$ and $He^4$. The present account will, however, be restricted to the properties of pure $He^3$ in the liquid and solid states. Pure $He^3$ has been obtained by the decay of the unstable hydrogen isotope tritium, produced by neutron irradiation of lithium. The gas is now available in the U.S.A. and the U.S.S.R. in quantities up to several litres (at N.T.P.), sufficient to determine the physical properties of $He^3$ and to provide the bath liquid for small scale cryostats as mentioned in Chapter I.

*Liquid* $He^3$. Liquid helium is a very light colourless substance. Its critical temperature is $3 \cdot 35°$ K. and its normal boiling point $3 \cdot 189°$ K. ($E_{55}$ scale). The density of the saturated liquid varies from $0 \cdot 06067$ gm./cm.$^3$ at $3 \cdot 135°$ K. to $0 \cdot 08121$ gm./cm.$^3$ at $1 \cdot 304°$ K. and a maximum of $0 \cdot 08172$ gm./cm.$^3$ at $0 \cdot 50°$ K. Thus the coefficient of expansion $\alpha$ is positive above $0 \cdot 5°$ K. and negative below this temperature but it is not yet known whether $\alpha$ passes through a minimum at about $0 \cdot 1°$ K. and becomes zero at $0°$ K. as predicted by Goldstein. The vapour pressure of the liquid varies from $769 \cdot 04$ mm. Hg at $3 \cdot 2°$ K. to $0 \cdot 1418$ mm. Hg at $0 \cdot 5°$ K. Liquid $He^3$ is therefore very suitable as the working substance in a vapour pressure thermometer for the temperature range $0 \cdot 5°-1 \cdot 0°$ K. where the vapour pressure of liquid $He^4$ is far too low. $He^3$ is still more volatile than $He^4$ as seen by the following values of the latent heat of vaporization determined by Roberts and Sydoriak and by Kerr: $5 \cdot 91$ cal./mol. at $3 \cdot 2°$ K., $11 \cdot 15$ cal./mol. at $2 \cdot 0°$ K., $9 \cdot 10$ cal./mol. at $1 \cdot 0°$ K. and $7 \cdot 36$ cal./mol. at $0 \cdot 54°$ K. These values are in good agreement with those calculated from the Clausius-Clapeyron equation using the experimental data for the liquid and vapour densities and the temperature variation of the saturated vapour pressure.

The specific heat of liquid $He^3$ has been determined from $2 \cdot 5$–$0 \cdot 085°$ K. It falls steadily over the whole temperature interval and at the lowest temperatures can be extrapolated linearly to zero at $0°$ K. There is no sign of a $\lambda$-phenomenon down to the lowest temperature investigated. It may be noted that the specific heat of liquid $He^3$ is much greater than that of liquid $He^4$ in the range of temperature $0.2–1.0°$ K., the ratio being about 250 at $0.5°$ K., and about 1950 at $0.25°$ K. The velocity of sound in liquid $He^3$ rises from 114·8 m./sec. at $3.0°$ K. to an extrapolated value of 183·4 m./sec. at $0°$ K. This is what is to be expected for low frequency sound in which $\omega\tau \ll 1$, where $\omega$ is the angular frequency of the sound wave and $\tau$ is the collision time in the liquid. The sound wave is a compressional wave and normal first sound results. When $\omega\tau$ approaches 1 the first sound will be greatly attenuated and Landau has shown that for $\omega\tau \gg 1$ a new kind of sound propagation will take place, 'zero sound', representing an oscillatory distortion of the constant energy surface in momentum space (Fermi surface). However, to generate zero sound at the highest frequency readily available, say 10 megacycles per sec., temperatures not higher than $0.01°$ K. will be required. No experimental test has been made of these predictions. The viscosity of liquid $He^3$ has been measured by Taylor and Dash using the oscillating disc method and by Zinov'eva using the capillary tube method. There is a discrepancy of about 20 per cent between the two sets of observations. According to Zinov'eva the viscosity rises from 16·1 $\mu$P at $3.2°$ K. to 48 $\mu$P at $0.35°$ K. Between $3.2°$ K. and $1.4°$ K. the rise is small, between $1.0°$ K. and $0.5°$ K. $\eta$ varies as $1/T^{1/2}$ and the curve becomes steeper below $0.5°$ K. suggesting that $\eta$ may vary as $1/T^2$ at very low temperatures as expected on the theory of a Fermi liquid. There is no sign of super-fluidity down to the lowest temperature yet investigated.

Since the $He^3$ atom has a non-zero nuclear magnetic moment and a nuclear spin of $\frac{1}{2}$, the liquid will exhibit a magnetic susceptibility which is temperature-dependent in contrast to liquid $He^4$. At relatively high temperatures the temperature-dependent part of the suscepti-bility may be expected to follow Curie's law, $\chi T=$ const., but when the temperature falls so that $kT$ is of the same order as the interaction energy of the $He^3$ nuclei, parallel or antiparallel alignment will set in and $\chi T$ will no longer be constant. Measurements have been made by Fairbank and his co-workers by means of the nuclear resonance method in which the area under the resonance curve is proportional to the magnetic susceptibility. For liquid $He^3$ at the saturated vapour pressure $\chi T$ was found to be constant down to about $1.0°$ K. and to decrease with decreasing temperature below this value (antiferromagnetic interaction). For liquid $He^3$ at pressures greater than the saturated vapour pressure and also for solid $He^3$ the deviation from constancy sets in at lower temperatures and $\chi T$ was greater, i.e. nearer to $\chi T = C$. This also means that the entropy of liquid $He^3$ increases with increase in pressure at the very low temperatures and that the entropy of liquid $He^3$ at, say $0.2°$ K., is less than that of solid $He^3$ at this temperature. This unusual feature is of much interest in interpreting the general physical properties of liquid and solid $He^3$.

*Solid* $He^3$. The melting curve of $He^3$ was determined by Osborne, Abraham and Weinstock in 1951 from $1.51°$ K. to $1.02°$ K. using the blocked capillary method and the temperature range was later extended by them to $0.16°$ K. Measurements were made in 1955 by Mills and Grilly up to $31°$ K. (3500 kg./cm.²). From $31°$ K. to $2°$ K. the melting pressure of $He^3$ can be represented by

$$p_m = 25.16 + 20.08 \, T^{1.517} \quad (p_m \text{ in atm.})$$

Again as with $He^4$ there is no tendency for the melting curve to intersect the vapour pressure curve at a triple point and $He^3$ remains liquid under its saturated vapour pressure down to $0°$ K.

Below $0.5°$ K. the observed melting pressures became independent of the temperature. Later work and later information from other sources showed that this result was not due to a lack of equilibrium between the $He^3$ and the paramagnetic salt. The observations could be accounted for if the melting pressure curve shows a minimum as predicted by Pomeranchuk on the basis of his theory of Fermi liquids. At temperatures below the minimum, the capillary will become blocked at a pressure corresponding to the minimum in the curve and the latter cannot be followed to still lower temperatures. This interpretation was confirmed by Daunt and his co-workers in 1959. They investigated the equilibrium of a mixture of solid and liquid $He^3$ in a sealed container at various temperatures and determined the pressure by means of a strain gauge attached to the outer wall of the elastic metal container. Their results showed conclusively the presence of a minimum at $T = 0.32°$ K. and $p_m = 29.3$ atm. The observed melting pressure rose steadily to 32 atm. at $0.07°$ K., showing no sign of the maximum expected by Bernades and Primakoff at about $0.1°$ K.

Below $p_m = 141$ kg./cm.$^2$, $T = 3.15°$ K. solid He$^3$ can crystallize in two different forms, a lower pressure, lower density phase, $\alpha$ which is body centred cubic and a higher pressure, higher density phase, which is hexagonal close packed. At temperature 1.9° K. and pressure 100 kg./cm.$^2$ the density of the $\alpha$ phase is 0.154 gm./cm.$^3$, while at temperature 3.3° K. and pressure 183 kg./cm.$^2$ the density of the $\beta$ phase is 0.172 gm./cm.$^3$. According to Pomeranchuk (1950) the temperature variation of the entropy of solid He$^3$ ($\alpha$ phase) below 1° K. may be expected to be as shown in the full curve of Fig. 17, where $S_{sol}$ is almost constant down to about

$$10^{-6}\text{--}10^{-7°}\text{ K.}$$

The contribution to the entropy of the thermal excitations is practically zero near 1° K. and the entropy almost wholly due to the random distribution of the nuclear spins. As the zero-point oscillations in the solid have an amplitude small compared with the interatomic distance the exchange interaction forces will only cause antiparallel alignment to set in at a very low temperature, estimated by Pomeranchuk to be $10^{-6}\text{--}10^{-7°}$ K. Below this temperature $S_{sol}$ will fall rapidly to zero. Later theories have suggested a higher temperature but as the susceptibility of solid He$^3$ at low densities follows Curie's law at least as low as 0.065° K. the rapid fall in entropy must occur at some still lower temperature.

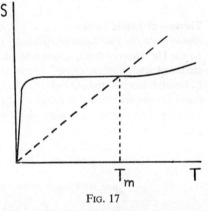

Fig. 17

On the other hand the experimentally observed variation of the entropy of liquid He$^3$ is represented by the dotted curve of Fig. 17 and the curves for solid and liquid intersect at some temperature below 0.5° K. From the Clausius-Clapeyron equation

$$\frac{dp_m}{dT} = \frac{S_{liq} - S_{sol}}{V_{liq} - V_{sol}}$$

where $p_m$ = melting pressure; $S_{liq}$, $S_{sol}$ = entropy of liquid, solid; $V_{liq}$, $V_{sol}$ = specific volume of liquid, solid and since the change of volume on melting, $V_{liq} - V_{sol}$ is known to be positive down to $0.3°$ K., the melting pressure–temperature curve will have a minimum where $S_{liq} = S_{sol}$. Furthermore, the latent heat of melting will change sign on passing through the minimum so that an adiabatic solidification by compression will lead to a fall in temperature. If Pomeranchuk's estimate of the temperature of the onset of nuclear alignment in solid $He^3$ should prove to be correct, temperatures of the order of $10^{-6°}$ K. should be reached in this way.

## Theories of Liquid Helium

*Liquid* $He^4$: *The Two Fluid Model and the Bose-Einstein Condensation*
As the $He^4$ atom contains an even number of fundamental particles, electrons and nucleons, $He^4$ obeys the Bose-Einstein statistics. F. London has pointed out that the ideal Bose-Einstein gas possesses many properties similar to those of the two-fluid model of He II. Thus for such a gas there exists a characteristic temperature $T_c$.

$$T_c = \frac{h^2}{2\pi m k}\left(\frac{N}{2\cdot612V}\right)^{2/3}$$

$N$ = number of molecules per mole

$V$ = volume of one mole

$m$ = mass of molecule

Below this temperature a finite fraction of the molecules passes into the lowest energy state with zero momentum. The number of molecules in the ground state is given by

$$n = N[1 - (T/T_c)^{3/2}]$$

for temperatures below $T_c$, whereas above $T_c$ the number of molecules in the ground state is of the order of one. Thus a condensation of molecules into the ground state begins at $T_c$ and is complete at $0°$ K., though the separation from the uncondensed molecules is only in *momentum space*. The condensed fluid has the properties of zero entropy and zero viscosity and has been identified by London with the *superfluid* of the two-fluid model. The uncondensed (or excited) molecules will then correspond to the *normal* fluid and their viscosity may be expected to be close to that of the *n*-component of He II on account of the low density and gas-like character of the latter.

If the figures for the mass of the $He^4$ atom and the molar density of liquid $He^4$ are inserted in the expression for $T_c$, the calculated value of the temperature is found to be $3 \cdot 13°$ K., not very different from the temperature of the $\lambda$-point, $T = 2 \cdot 172°$ K.

The specific heat of an ideal Bose-Einstein gas shows a peak at $T_c$ (discontinuity in the slope, third-order transition) and so does not agree well with the actual behaviour of $C_s$ for $He^4$ at the $\lambda$-point. Since liquid $He^4$ is certainly not an ideal gas, various attempts have been made to introduce arbitrary modifications into the theory in the hope of producing a better agreement with the observed properties of liquid $He^4$. The results have not been very convincing.

The solution of the actual problem of a Bose-Einstein system of interacting particles is very difficult and progress has only recently been made, particularly by the work of Huang and Yang and Lee.

*Theory of a Bose-Einstein liquid.* Instead of the direct approach mentioned above Landau has attacked the problem of a quantum liquid in a different way. He considers liquid $He^4$ as a background fluid in which, at any temperature above $0°$ K., there are elementary excitations. These excitations belong to the liquid as a whole and not to the individual atoms as in the theory of the ideal Bose-Einstein gas. The excitations can be regarded as forming a gas of quasi-particles and when the temperature is low enough and so the density of excitations is low, interactions between the quasi-particles can be neglected. Landau postulates the energy spectrum of the excitations to have the form shown in Fig. 18, a form consistent with the known properties of a Bose-Einstein system. Near the origin the energy $\epsilon(p)$ is a linear function of the momentum $p$:

$$\epsilon(p) = u_1 p$$

where $u_1$ is the velocity of first sound in the liquid. These excitations are longitudinal sound waves and are known as *phonons*.

At higher values of the momentum $\epsilon(p)$ shows first a maximum, then a minimum and finally increases steadily with increase in $p$.

5

The excitations in the neighbourhood of the minimum are characterized by:

$$\epsilon(p) = \Delta + \frac{(p-p_0)^2}{2\mu}$$

where $\Delta = \epsilon(p_0)$ and $\mu$ is the 'effective mass' of the excitation. These excitations, to which the name *rotons* is given, have been shown by

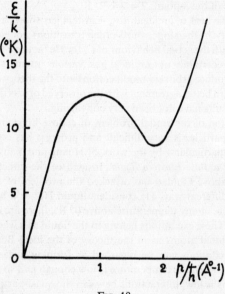

FIG. 18

Feynman to be analogous to vortex rings in the liquid with an inner diameter of the order of magnitude of the interatomic spacing in the liquid.

At any temperature below $0.6°$ K. the excitations will be exclusively phonons and the specific heat will be given by

$$C_{ph} = \frac{16\pi^5 k^4 T^3}{15h^3 \rho u_1^3}$$

This agrees well with the data of Wiebes, Niels-Hakkenberg and Kramers and of Markham, Pearce, Netzel and Dillinger using the known velocity of sound extrapolated to 0° K. At 1·0° K. both phonons and rotons are excited and the specific heat consists of the above phonon contribution and a roton contribution, $C_r$, where

$$C_r = \frac{2\mu^{1/2}p_0^2\Delta^2(2\pi)^{3/2}}{\rho k^{1/2}h^3T^{3/2}}\left[1+\frac{kT}{\Delta}+\frac{3}{4}\left(\frac{kT}{\Delta}\right)^2\right]e^{-\Delta/kT}$$

Landau's theory reproduces accurately the observed specific heat up to about 1·3° K. with the following values of the constants:

$$\Delta/k = 8\cdot9°\,\mathrm{K}., p_0/\hbar = 1\cdot96\,\text{Å}^{-1}, \mu/m = 0\cdot23$$

($m=$ mass of helium atom).

Above 1·3° K. the number of excitations is increasing so rapidly with increase in temperature that the excitations can no longer be treated as non-interacting.

From a detailed discussion of the necessary properties of the wave function of liquid He$^4$ and of the spacial distribution of the atoms in the liquid (the structure factor which can be determined experimentally by the scattering of X-rays or neutrons), Feynman has shown that the energy spectrum of He$^4$ must have the form postulated by Landau. A neutron can be inelastically scattered by liquid He$^4$ so as to excite a single excitation. By studying the loss in energy of a beam of neutrons as a function of their momentum, various workers have been able to evaluate the energy spectrum experimentally from a point where the $\epsilon(p)$ relation is almost linear, through the maximum and the minimum to a point where at high momentum the curve is increasing steadily. The values of the constants are in excellent agreement with those quoted above.

Landau considers the case where the background fluid at 0° K., and therefore free from thermal excitations, is flowing through a tube with a velocity $v$. The energy of the fluid can only be changed and the fluid slowed down by the creation of excitations by interaction with the walls. For an excitation to be created the velocity of the fluid must be greater than $|\epsilon/p|$, where $p$ is the momentum of the excitation parallel to the wall. The flow will therefore be resistanceless up to a critical velocity $v_c = |\epsilon/p|$. For phonons $v_c$ becomes $2\cdot4 \times 10^2$ cm./sec. and for rotons $v_c$ is $6 \times 10^3$ cm./sec. The above argument also holds for temperatures above $0°$ K. Thus for small velocities of flow the background fluid has the properties of the *superfluid* of the two-fluid model.† The critical velocities observed in liquid He$^4$ are all much smaller than $v_c$ calculated as above and it is believed that they correspond to the creation of other types of excitation with smaller values of $|\epsilon/p|$.

The behaviour of the existing excitations in the moving fluid at a temperature other than $0°$ K., must also be considered. Let the liquid be moving with a velocity $v_s$ relative to a fixed observer and let the excitations have a drift velocity $v_n$ relative to the observer. An excitation, which has an energy $\epsilon$ when stationary, has an energy $\epsilon_0 = \epsilon + p \cdot v$ in a liquid moving with a velocity $v$. So the equilibrium distribution of the excitations is given by the Bose-Einstein expression

$$n(\epsilon) = [\exp \beta(\epsilon_0 - p \cdot v_n) - 1]^{-1}$$
$$= [\exp \beta(\epsilon + p \cdot v_s - p \cdot v_n) - 1]^{-1}$$

The net momentum associated with the excitations is then

$$\bar{p} = \int p \, [\exp \beta(\epsilon + p \cdot v_s - p \cdot v_n) - 1]^{-1} h^{-3} d^3 p$$

Then if $v_s$ and $v_n$ are small an expansion to first-order terms gives

$$\bar{p} = -\rho_n(v_s - v_n)$$

where

$$\rho_n = -\tfrac{1}{3}\beta \int p^2 [\exp \beta \epsilon - 1]^{-2} \exp \beta \epsilon h^{-3} d^3 p$$

Thus the total momentum of the liquid per unit volume will be

$$j = \rho v_s + \bar{p} = \rho v_s - \rho_n(v_s - v_n)$$

or with

$$\rho = \rho_s + \rho_n$$

$$j = \rho_s v_s + \rho_n v_n$$

The momentum per unit volume is the sum of the momentum of the background fluid and that of the excitations. So the gas of excitations behaves as the normal component of the two-fluid model

† Thus superfluidity may be expected in any liquid for which the slope of the $p, \epsilon$ curve is finite at the origin. This is not the case for a Fermi liquid and so superfluidity is not to be expected in He$^3$ on this basis.

and the above calculations provides the required justification of the model together with a means of calculating $\rho_n$ as a function of the temperature.

The existence of a $\lambda$-point in liquid $He^4$ is not explicit in the Landau theory. However, the value of $\rho_n$ increases so rapidly at higher temperatures that if one extrapolates beyond the strict limit of validity of the formula to the point $\rho_n/\rho = 1$, the temperature at which this occurs is found to be $2\cdot5°$ K., a fairly close approximation to the actual $\lambda$-point.

The viscosity of the normal component of liquid He II has been calculated by Landau and Khalatnikov by considering the excitations as particles with definite collision cross-sections and mean free paths and applying the methods of the kinetic theory of gases. The theory is complicated but the final result agrees well with the observed values of $\eta_n$ at temperatures below $1\cdot6°$ K. provided that certain plausible assumptions are made with regard to the quantities which cannot be calculated directly.

## Liquid $He^3$ and the Ideal Fermi Gas

The atom of $He^3$, as a free particle with spin $1/2$, obeys the Fermi-Dirac statistics. In view of the initial success of the application of the theory of an ideal Bose-Einstein gas to the explanation of the two fluid model of liquid $He^4$, it was reasonable to compare the known properties of liquid $He^3$ with those of an ideal Fermi gas. The latter were familiar from their application to the case of the conduction electrons in metals. (See Chapters IV and V.) The internal energy $U$ and the specific heat $C_v$ per mole of an ideal Fermi gas are

$$U = \tfrac{3}{2}RT \frac{F_{3/2}(\eta)}{F_{1/2}(\eta)}$$

$$C_v = \tfrac{3}{4}R\left(\frac{5F_{3/2}(\eta)}{F_{1/2}(\eta)} - \frac{3F_{1/2}(\eta)}{F'_{1/2}(\eta)}\right)$$

where
$$F_k(\eta) = \frac{1}{k!} \int\limits_0^\infty \frac{x^k}{e^{x-\eta}+1}\,dx$$

are functions associated with the Fermi distribution.

For large values of $\eta$ we have

$$U = \frac{3R\epsilon_0}{5k}\left\{1 + \tfrac{5}{12}\pi^2\frac{kT}{\epsilon_0} + \ldots\right\}$$

$$C_v \simeq 4\cdot93R\left(\frac{kT}{\epsilon_0}\right)$$

where
$$\epsilon_0 = kT_0 = \frac{h^2}{8}\left(\frac{3\rho}{\pi}\right)^{2/3}\left(\frac{1}{m}\right)^{5/3}$$

With the density $\rho$ and mass $m$ corresponding to liquid He$^3$, the degeneracy temperature is found to be about 5° K. At 0° K. all energy states up to the Fermi energy $\epsilon_0$ are occupied and at any finite temperature a few states just below $\epsilon_0$ are empty and a few states above $\epsilon_0$ are occupied.

The curve of $C_v$ for $T_0 = 5°$ K. is in agreement as regards order of magnitude with the observed specific heat of liquid He$^3$ between 3° K. and 1° K. but not as regards detailed variations with temperature. In the ideal Fermi gas there is of course, no indication of a specific heat anomaly such as occurs with He$^4$ and no sign of superfluidity in any of the physical properties.

For an ideal Fermi gas with a nuclear magnetic moment $\mu$ the susceptibility at $T \gg T_0$ has the usual Curie law value $\chi = n\mu^2/kT$ but for $T \ll T_0$, the susceptibility becomes constant and equal to $\chi = 3n\mu^2/2kT_0$. Fairbank's observations on liquid He$^3$ at the saturated vapour pressure agree with the susceptibility calculated for an ideal Fermi gas with a degeneracy temperature of 0·45° K. These and other later comparisons with experimental data showed that the ideal Fermi gas is a very poor model for liquid He$^3$ and is indeed misleading.

*Theory of a Fermi liquid.* To understand the physical properties of liquid He$^3$ a theory of a system of interacting Fermi particles, thus a Fermi liquid, is needed. Attempts have been made by Brueckner and Gammel and by Landau. As the subject is one of too great complexity to be dealt with in any detail in this monograph an outline only of the ideas of Landau will be given.

As in the case of the Bose liquid Landau considers the excitations in a background fluid but shows that in the Fermi liquid the interaction of the excitations is important. The excitations cannot therefore always be treated as an ideal gas. The theory is based on two assumptions: (1) The classification of the energy states of a Fermi liquid corresponds to that of non-interacting atoms as a gradual switching-on of the interactions between previously non-interacting particles does not disturb this classification. The excitations become quasi-particles, each with a different energy and the number of quasi-particles is equal to that of the atoms. (2) The interaction of the quasi-particles can be taken into account as a self-consistent field of the surrounding quasi-particles. This results in the energy of the system not being equal to the sum of the energies of the quasi-particles. The distribution function has the same form as that of an ideal Fermi gas

$$n(\epsilon) = 1/\exp\{(\epsilon - \mu)/kT\} + 1$$

but now the energy is a functional of $n(\epsilon)$ so that the above expression is an implicit definition of $n(\epsilon)$.

The theory leads to a linear variation of the specific heat at lowest temperatures as observed and in this region the quasi-particles have an effective mass $m^* = p\partial\epsilon/\partial p$. The observations of Daunt et al. lead to $m^* = 1\cdot84m$, where $m$ is the mass of the He$^3$ atom.

The observed constant susceptibility at lowest temperatures is much larger than that of an ideal Fermi gas. This is due to the presence of exchange interactions which leads to a parallelism of the nuclear spins together with the anti-parallelism due to the Pauli exclusion principle. A small increase in strength of the exchange interaction would make liquid He$^3$ nuclear ferromagnetic. The theory leads to a $T^{-2}$ variation of the viscosity of liquid He$^3$ and to the absence of superfluidity.

The theory is valid only for those temperatures at which the indeterminacy in the energy of the quasi-particles due to their collisions is smaller than the average excitation energy, $kT \gg \hbar/\tau$, where $\tau$ is the time between collisions and is proportional to $T^{-2}$. For liquid He$^3$ this means that only observations below $0\cdot1°$ K. can be compared with the theory. So far very few observations exist within this range of temperature.

The above statements only hold if the attractive interaction between the quasi-particles, which tends to cause a condensation into a lower energy state with correlations between pairs of quasi-particles with equal and opposite momenta, is not important. It can, however, be expected that at extremely low temperatures this condensation will occur as in the case of electrons in superconductors. The new state will differ, however, in some ways from superconductivity, and it remains to be seen whether liquid He$^3$ will exhibit superfluidity at temperatures not yet reached.

# CHAPTER IV

# Specific Heats

The specific heats of gases and solids will now be discussed as an example of calorimetry at low temperatures.

### Gases

Two general methods have been employed for the determination of the specific heat of gases down to very low temperatures, the continuous flow method and the Nernst-Eucken method, using compressed gas at moderate pressures.

TABLE 4

| Substance | $T (^{\circ}C.)$ | $C_{p_0}$ | $C_{v_0}$ |
|-----------|------------------|-----------|-----------|
| He | $+18$ | 4·993 | 3·008 |
|    | $-180$ | 4·934 | 2·949 |
| $H_2$ | $+16$ | 6·860 | 4·875 |
|       | $-76$ | 6·364 | 4·379 |
|       | $-181$ | 5·320 | 3·335 |
| $N_2$ | $+20$ | 6·969 | 4·984 |
|       | $-181$ | 6·718 | 4·733 |

In the continuous flow method the gas flows at a constant rate through a cooling coil immersed in a constant temperature bath. It then flows over an electric heater supplying a known amount of heat per sec., and its temperature rise is measured by means of a platinum resistance thermometer. The results are shown in Table 4. $C_{p_0}$ is the specific heat at constant pressure corrected for the deviations from the ideal gas law. $C_{v_0}$ is obtained from the (corrected) observed $C_p$, using well-known thermodynamical formulae. It will be seen that while the specific heat of the monatomic gas helium remains fairly constant, that of the diatomic gases falls considerably with decrease in temperature.

In the determinations of $C_v$ by Eucken and Hiller the gas was enclosed at moderate pressure in a small steel cylinder inside a vacuum chamber as in Fig. 19.

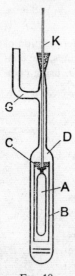

FIG. 19

The general trend of the variation of the specific heats of diatomic molecules will be illustrated by the case of hydrogen. The earlier results of Eucken (1912) are given in Table 5, and are plotted along with those of Eucken and Hiller and others (for $C_R$, see later) in Fig. 20. It will be seen from Table 5 that the specific heat of hydrogen falls off rapidly with decrease in temperature and becomes nearly constant and equal to 2·98 below 60° K.

The classical theory indicates that a gas possesses an energy $\frac{1}{2}RT$ per deg. of freedom per gm. mol. The contribution to the specific heat $C_v$ of the translational energy is therefore $\frac{3}{2}R = 2·98$ cal./gm. mol. deg. and the specific heat at constant volume of monatomic gases should have this value. The results of Scheel and Heuse show that this is approximately the case with He and A. Below 60° K. hydrogen thus behaves as a monatomic gas in that only the translational energy contributes to $C_v$. In general, however, a diatomic molecule will also possess rotational energy and classically the contribution of the rotation to the specific heat $C_R$, will be $\frac{2}{2}R$ and therefore independent of the temperature. According to the quantum theory the rotational energy of a diatomic molecule is

$$E_R = n(n+1)\frac{h^2}{8\pi^2 I}$$

in which $I$ is the moment of inertia and the quantum number $n$ may have the values 0, 1, 2, 3, etc. At very low temperatures only the lowest rotational state ($n = 0$ or 1 according to the type of molecule) will be occupied and the higher states will only begin to be occupied as the temperature rises. $C_R$ will therefore vary with temperature. It can be shown that $C_R$ for a diatomic molecule is given by

$$C_R = \sigma^2 R \frac{d^2}{d\sigma^2}(\log Q) \tag{1}$$

in which $\sigma = h^2/8\pi^2 I k T$ and $Q$ is a function of $\sigma$.

TABLE 5

| $T(^\circ K.)$ | $C_{v_0}$ |
|---|---|
| 196·5 | 4·39 |
| 100 | 3·42 |
| 80 | 3·14 |
| 60 | 2·99 |
| 45 | 3·00 |
| 35 | 2·98 |

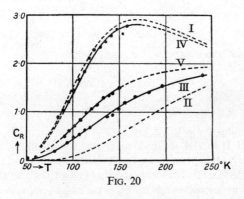

FIG. 20

By subtracting 2·98 from the observed values of $C_v$ one can obtain $C_R$ from Eucken's results.† When the experimental values were compared with expression (1) no satisfactory agreement could be

† Eucken's observations show that $C_v$ falls below 2·98 at about 20° K. This result, which is known as the degeneration of gases, can be explained by applying the quantum theory to the translational energy of the molecules. Helium shows a similar result.

obtained with any value of $I$. Later, however, the wave mechanics indicated that hydrogen should exist in two forms, *ortho-* and *para-*hydrogen, which differ in the magnetic moments of the nuclei of the two hydrogen atoms being parallel in *ortho-*hydrogen and antiparallel in *para-*hydrogen. Furthermore, theory showed that at room temperature ordinary hydrogen consists of a mixture of *ortho-* and *para-*hydrogen in the ratio 3:1 and that the transformation of the one form into the other is very slow at that temperature. Dennison was then able to show that Eucken's results for $C_R$ could be explained satisfactorily by supposing that no transformation of *ortho-* into *para-*hydrogen took place during the time required to make the observations, and that therefore the two forms could be taken as independent. The specific heat of ordinary hydrogen then becomes

$$C_R = \frac{\rho C_{R(p)} + C_{R(o)}}{1 + \rho} \tag{2}$$

in which $\rho = \frac{1}{3}$, and

$$C_{R(p)} = \sigma^2 R \frac{d^2}{d\sigma^2} (\log Q_{(p)}) \tag{3}$$

with          $Q_{(p)} = 1 + 5e^{-6\sigma} + 9e^{-20\sigma} + \ldots$

corresponding to $n = 0, 2, 4$, etc., and

$$C_{R(o)} = \sigma^2 R \frac{d^2}{d\sigma^2} (\log Q_{(o)}) \tag{4}$$

with          $Q_{(o)} = 3e^{-2\sigma} + 7e^{-12\sigma} + 11e^{-30\sigma} + \ldots$

corresponding to $n = 1, 3, 5$, etc.

Curves I, II and III of Fig. 20 represent expressions (3), (4) and (2) respectively, taking I to be $4 \cdot 64 \times 10^{-41}$, a value in good agreement with that deduced by Hori from spectra ($4 \cdot 67 \times 10^{-41}$). It will be seen that the experimental values for $C_R$ in the case of ordinary hydrogen agree well with curve III.

It has also been found possible by keeping hydrogen for a considerable time at a low temperature with or without a catalyst to increase the *para-*hydrogen content and even to obtain pure *para-*hydrogen. Curves IV and V represent the theoretical course of $C_R$ for mixtures of higher *para-*hydrogen content, the experimental points being Eucken and Hiller's observations on these mixtures. It will be seen that the theory can reproduce the experimental results in a very satisfactory way.

Since the molecule of deuterium (the heavier isotope of hydrogen with mass 2) is also symmetrical it also exists in *ortho*- and *para*-modifications. Normal deuterium consists of a mixture of *ortho*- and *para*-deuterium in the ratio 2:1. Even quantum numbers $n$ are associated with $o$-$D_2$ and odd numbers with $p$-$D_2$ since deuterium obeys Bose-Einstein statistics while hydrogen obeys Fermi-Dirac statistics. The curve of $C_R$ for $p$-$D_2$ is similar to that of $o$-$H_2$, while that of $C_R$ for $o$-$D_2$ shows a maximum like $p$-$H_2$ but at about 85° K. instead of 170° K.

The rotational specific heat of other diatomic gases which consist of only one molecular species can be theoretically accounted for by formula (1) with the appropriate value of $I$.

At low temperatures the vibrations of the atoms in the molecule are not excited, and so the contribution of the vibrational energy to the specific heat of gases will not be considered here.

## Solids

The specific heat of solids at low temperatures have been determined almost exclusively by means of the vacuum calorimeter developed by Nernst and Eucken. The calorimeter is differently constructed according to the nature of the substance to be investigated. Fig. 21 shows the arrangement used by Keesom for determining the specific heat of metals at hydrogen and helium temperatures. The specimen is in the shape of a cylindrical block into which is screwed a core containing an electrical heater H and a resistance thermometer T. The whole is suspended inside a metal chamber which can be evacuated. The experimental results show that the specific heats of solids, apart from the special cases discussed later, vary with the temperature in the general way shown in Fig. 22, falling from a value of approximately 6 cal./deg. gm. atom (for the elements) at high temperatures to very small values at helium temperatures (0·000254 cal./deg. gm. atom for Ag at 1·35° K.) to become zero at the absolute zero.

According to the classical mechanics the atomic heat (specific heat × atomic weight) of a monatomic solid element should be independent of the temperature and equal to $3R$ or approximately 6 cal./deg. The explanation of the observed fall in the specific heat of solids at low temperatures was one of the early successes of the quantum theory. By assuming that all the atoms in the solid were vibrating with a frequency $\nu$ (due to their thermal motions) and attributing to each of the three degrees of freedom of the atom an energy

$$E = h\nu/(e^{h\nu/kT} - 1)$$

as required by the quantum theory in place of $kT$ ($\frac{1}{2}kT$ potential energy $+ \frac{1}{2}kT$ kinetic energy), Einstein obtained the following formula for the atomic heat at constant volume $C_v = (\partial E/\partial T)_v$:

$$C_v = 3R \cdot \frac{e^{\theta/T}(\theta/T)^2}{(e^{\theta/T}-1)^2} \quad (5)$$

$\theta = h\nu/k, R = Nk, N =$ number of atoms in gm. atom. This expression gives a good qualitative representation of the variation of the specific heat of solids† with the temperature. By discarding the too simple assumption that all the atoms vibrate with the same frequency $\nu$, Debye was able to deduce a formula which gives a generally very satisfactory representation of the experimental results down to very low temperatures,

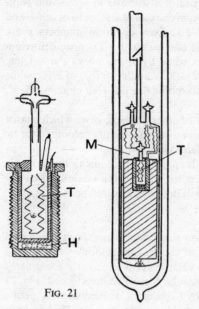

FIG. 21

$$C_v = 3R \left\{ 12\left(\frac{T}{\theta_D}\right)^3 \int_0^{\nu_m} \frac{x^3}{e^x-1} dx - \frac{3\theta_D/T}{e^{\theta_D/T}-1} \right\} \quad (6)$$

in which $x = h\nu/kT$, $\theta_D = h\nu_m/k$.

† The experimentally determined quantity is $C_p$. $C_v$ can be obtained from $C_p$ by means of several thermodynamical or empirical formulae, such as $C_p - C_v = TV\alpha^2/\chi$ in which $\alpha =$ coefficient of cubic expansion, $\chi =$ compressibility and $V =$ atomic volume.

All frequencies from 0 up to a maximum value $v_m$ are now taken to be possible, and the energy of the solid becomes

$$E = \int\limits_{0}^{v_m} \{hv/(e^{hv/kT}-1)\}\, n(v)\, dv$$

in which $n(v)\, dv$ is the number of frequencies lying within the range $v$ to $v+dv$. Debye considers the substance as a homogeneous elastic solid and assumes that the thermal motions of the atoms can be represented by the sum of all the possible elastic waves which can occur in the solid. From the theory of elasticity the number of independent vibrations (elastic waves) whose frequencies lie between $v$ and $v+dv$ can be calculated. In order to determine the maximum frequency $v_m$, Debye equates the total number of independent vibrations possessed by one gram atom of the solid to $3N$, the total number of degrees of freedom. (For an infinitely extended solid the number of independent vibrations would be infinite.) Then

$$\int\limits_{0}^{v_m} n(v)\, dv = 3N$$

In this way, using the value of $n(v)$ given by elastic theory, the magnitude of $\theta_D = hv_m/k$ can be calculated. Debye thus obtains the expression

$$\theta_D = \frac{3 \cdot 6 \times 10^{-3}}{A^{1/3} \rho^{1/6} \chi^{1/2} [f(\sigma)]^{1/3}}$$

where $A =$ atomic weight, $\rho =$ density, $\chi =$ compressibility and $\sigma =$ Poisson's ratio.

Table 6 illustrates the degree of agreement between the observations on aluminium and the atomic heat calculated using $\theta_D = 398°$ K. Table 7 gives the values of $\theta_D$ for a number of elements, columns 2 and 3, the experimental value deduced from the observed specific heat at the higher temperatures and at very low temperatures respectively, column 4 the calculated values using Debye's expression, columns 5 and 6 theoretical values calculated from formulae given by Grüneisen (from coefficient of cubic expansion) and Lindemann (from melting point) respectively.

In comparing the observed values with the calculated for the specific heat of compounds the comparison may be made, except at very low temperatures, by combining a Debye curve (to represent the contribution to the specific heat of the translational motion of the molecules as a whole) and an Einstein curve (to represent the contribution of the internal vibrations of the molecule, which can be supposed to occur with definite frequency or frequencies deducible from the properties of the molecule).

TABLE 6

*Aluminium* $\theta_D = 398° K.$

| $T(°K.)$ | $C_p$ (obs.) | $C_p$ (calc.) |
|----------|--------------|---------------|
| 32·4     | 0·25         | 0·25          |
| 35·1     | 0·33         | 0·32          |
| 83·0     | 2·41         | 2·36          |
| 86·0     | 2·52         | 2·50          |
| 88·3     | 2·62         | 2·59          |
| 137·0    | 3·97         | 4·10          |
| 235·0    | 5·32         | 5·34          |
| 331·0    | 5·82         | 5·78          |
| 433·0    | 6·10         | 6·07          |
| 555·0    | 6·48         | 6·30          |

According to expression (6) the specific heats of all solids which satisfy the assumptions of the theory, should lie on the same curve if plotted against $T/\theta_D$. Schrödinger has shown that the observed specific heats of a large number of solids do indeed lie fairly accurately on this curve.†

† The curve, together with the experimental points, is reproduced, for example in Roberts, *Heat and Thermodynamics*, data being given for Al, Ag, C, Ca, Cd, Cu, Fe, Hg, I, Na, Pb, Tl, Zn, CaF₂, NaCl, KBr, KCl. The very numerous experimental points are omitted from Fig. 22 as they cannot be adequately shown on a small diagram.

At sufficiently low temperature, $T < \theta_D/12$, Debye's formula reduces to

$$C_v = 464 \cdot 5 \left(\frac{T}{\theta_D}\right)^3 = \text{const.} \times T^3 \qquad (7)$$

This simple expression fits fairly well the experimental values for a large number of substances (but for comment see later) and is of

TABLE 7

| Element | $\theta_D$ (expt.) | | $\theta_D$ (calc.) | | |
|---|---|---|---|---|---|
| | Higher temps. | Very low temps. | Debye | Grüneisen | Lindemann |
| Ag | 217 | 210 | 212 | 210 | 196 |
| Cu | 315 | 320 | 329 | 325 | 302 |
| Cd | 160 | 129 | 168 | 148 | 123 |
| Al | 398 | 385 | 399 | 374 | 342 |
| Pb | 88 | 84 | 72 | 103 | 82 |
| C (diamond) | 1840 | 2230 | – | 1860 | 1450 |

importance as it has been used extensively to extrapolate to the absolute zero in cases where the heat content of solids, $\int_0^T C_v dT$, is required. Since the internal vibrations of the molecules of any substance are not excited below a certain temperature dependent on the nature of the substance, the Debye $T^3$ law should hold whether the substance is an element or a compound provided this characteristic temperature is not exceeded. Summarizing, it may be said that the Debye theory is a very good first approximation to a satisfactory theory of the specific heats of solids, but too much must not be expected of it. In particular, small discrepancies between calculated and observed values should not be ascribed to the presence of additional sources of energy unless independent confirmatory evidence can be furnished for this interpretation.

A comparison between the predictions of the Debye theory and experimentally determined specific heats may be conveniently made by plotting the value of $\theta_D$ calculated for each experimental point against the temperature. Deviations from a horizontal straight line indicate disagreements between theory and experiment. Such discrepancies may be due to (i) inadequacies in the Debye theory itself, or (ii) contributions to the specific heat from types of energy other than the lattice vibrations. This latter contribution can be eliminated provided a satisfactory theory of the effect is available. The $\theta_D.T$ curve so

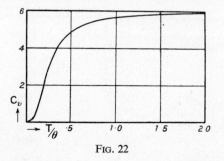

FIG. 22

obtained usually contains a horizontal straight part at the lowest temperatures followed by a minimum and then a slow rise to an almost horizontal part at high temperatures. The initial constant value of $\theta_D$ occurs in a region where the specific heat is accurately proportional to $T^3$ (for example KCl, which may be regarded as a simple cubic lattice of argon-like ions, from $1\cdot2$–$4\cdot2°$ K.; $\theta_D = 233 \pm 3°$ K., Keesom and Pearlman (1953)) although this law is valid for temperatures less than $\theta_D/50$ rather than $\theta_D/12$ as deduced by Debye.

The least satisfactory feature of the Debye theory is the calculation of the *vibration spectrum* of the solid from the elastic properties of a continuum instead of those of a lattice of discrete points (atoms or ions). A method by which the vibrational frequencies of such a lattice can be determined was published in 1912 by Born and von Karman, but on account of the very tedious calculations involved no values were given for the specific heat of any particular substance. The calculations of the vibration spectrum of crystal lattices of the simple cubic, face-centred cubic, body-centred cubic and diamond types have now been carried out by Blackman, Kellerman, Smith, Leighton and others. The various spectra differ in detail but all contain the general features that the $n(\nu)$–$\nu$ curve first rises to a rather broad maximum then falls to a minimum and finally rises to a sharp high maximum before falling to zero at $\nu_m$. When the expression

$$\phi(r) = 1 \cdot 63 \times 10^{-7} r^{-12} - 1 \cdot 05 \times 10^{-10} r^{-6}$$

(Domb and Zucker, 1956) for the potential energy of two argon atoms at a distance $r$ apart is put into the calculations of Leighton for the face-centred cubic lattice, a spectrum is obtained from which the calculated specific heat agrees very well with the experimentally determined values for solid argon; Hill (1954), 3–20° K., and Figgins (1955), 16–35° K.

The theories of the lattice specific heat are based on the assumption that all the atoms or molecules remain throughout in the lowest electronic level. If there is also another possible level of the electronic energy higher by an amount $\Delta E$ than the ground state, then at absolute zero all the atoms or molecules will be in the lower level but as the temperature rises the upper state will also become populated. The number of atoms in the upper state at any temperature $T$ is given by $n = n_0 e^{-\Delta E/kT}$, where $n_0$ is the number of atoms in the lower state, so that at a temperature for which $kT$ is very large compared with $\Delta E$ there will be an equal number of atoms in each state. Some of the heat put into the solid will therefore go into raising some of the atoms from the ground state to the upper state and the apparent specific heat will consequently be greater than the lattice specific heat alone. Schottky has shown that the additional term in the specific heat $\Delta C$ which results from increasing the population of the upper state is given by

$$\Delta C = \frac{k(\Delta E/kT)^2 e^{\Delta E/kT}}{(1 + e^{\Delta E/kT})^2} \tag{8}$$

The specific heats of certain rare-earth metals, rare-earth compounds and solid *ortho*-hydrogen show anomalies which can be represented by an expression similar to (8) but generalized for the case in which there are several upper levels with separations $\Delta E_1$, $\Delta E_2$, etc., and in which the levels have different statistical weights. The results show, however, the difficulty of making a quite definite analysis of the specific heat observations. The specific heat of neodymium sulphate, $Nd_2(SO_4)_3.8H_2O$, has been measured by Ahlberg, Blanchard and Lundberg between 3° K. and 40° K., showing an anomaly with a maximum at about 25° K. while the measurements of Kurti, of Giauque and MacDougall and of Clark and Keesom on gadolinium sulphate, $Gd_2(SO_4)_3.8H_2O$ result in a very pronounced maximum† at 0·26° K. The value of $\Delta C$ in each case is best determined by subtracting the specific heat of the corresponding lanthanum salt, which is diamagnetic and so does not show a Schottky effect, from the observed specific heat. Ahlberg, Blanchard and Lundberg state that $\Delta C$ for the neodymium salt agrees with the presence of a level of statistical weight 4 situated 77 cm.$^{-1}$‡ above the ground state. At the time it was believed that the crystalline field§ of the rare earth sulphates had cubic symmetry. In such a field the ground state of the $Nd^{+++}$ ion ($^4I_{9/2}$) would be split into three levels with statistical weights 2, 4 and 4 and Spedding's analysis of the absorption spectrum of neodymium sulphate at low temperatures had shown the presence of levels with relative positions 0, 77, 260 cm.$^{-1}$. If these are identified with the predicted levels there appears to be excellent agreement between the specific heat, the crystalline field theory and the absorption spectrum as the contribution to the specific heat from the level at 260 cm.$^{-1}$ would be negligible at low temperatures. Penney and Kynch and later Elliott and Stevens have, however, shown that the susceptibilities of the rare earth sulphates cannot be explained by a cubic crystalline field. The susceptibilities of single crystals of neodymium sulphate indicate the presence of a level at 40 cm.$^{-1}$, and if this level is doubly degenerate it can explain the specific heat observations just as well as a quadruple level at 77 cm.$^{-1}$. Penney and Kynch showed that if the crystalline field has both fourth-order and sixth-order terms and not merely

† The specific heat rises to 1·6 cal./gm. mol. deg. at 0·3° K. although the contribution due to the lattice energy at this temperature is only $3 \times 10^{-6}$ cal./gm. mol. deg.

‡ 1 cm.$^{-1}$ = 2·92 cal. = $1.23 \times 10^{-4}$ eV.

§ See Chapter VI for the effect of the crystalline field on the levels of paramagnetic ions.

fourth-order (cubic), the ground level of the $Nd^{+++}$ would split into three levels of statistical weights 4, 2 and 4 as now required.

The gadolinium sulphate results were first analysed in terms of eight equally spaced levels and later in terms of a cubic field type of splitting of the ground state $^8S_{7/2}$ of the $Gd^{+++}$ ion into three closely spaced levels of statistical weight 2, 4 and 2 at positions 0, 0·61 cm.$^{-1}$, 0·98 cm.$^{-1}$. It is, however, now known that the splitting pattern consists of four levels each of statistical weight 2, situated at 0, 0·2, 0·48 and 0·82 cm.$^{-1}$.

Schottky anomalies in the specific heat are also to be found in the salts used in adiabatic demagnetization but at temperatures well below 1° K. Thus the data from which the $T^*–T$ curve of ferric ammonium alum (Fig. 9) was plotted can be used to calculate the $C_v–T$ curve. This curve shows a Schottky anomaly, due to the splitting of the ground state by the crystalline field with a maximum at about 0·075° K. At still lower temperatures the $C_v$-$T$ curve shows a high $\lambda$-type anomaly with a maximum at about 0·04° K. This is due to the co-operative process which sets in at the Néel point where the paramagnetism of the salt changes to antiferromagnetism.†

The measurements of Simon, Mendelssohn and Ruhemann on solid hydrogen between 2° K. and 20° K. show that while solid *para*-hydrogen obeys the Debye law for $C_s$ with $\theta_D = 91$, the specific heat of solid *ortho*-hydrogen (deduced from measurements on mixtures of known proportions of *ortho*-hydrogen and *para*-hydrogen) deviates markedly below 12° K. The specific heat curve can be explained if it is assumed that the *ortho*-molecules in the solid state possess three energy states distant 2·56 cm.$^{-1}$ from each other. Later measurements by Hill indicate that the specific heat anomaly may not be purely of the Schottky type, but may also include a contribution of the co-operative type (see next paragraph).

Another type of deviation from the Debye curve, which deserves mention, is that shown by solid methane, solid hydrogen bromide and various ammonium salts. Clusius has shown that the specific heat of solid methane begins to rise very rapidly with rise in temperature in the neighbourhood of 20° K., reaches a maximum of more than 80 cal./gm. mol. deg. at 20·4° K. and then falls rapidly to about 4·6 at 21·2° K. The specific heat–temperature curve then becomes normal

† See Chapter VI.

up to the melting point. The anomaly is therefore similar in shape to that shown by liquid helium but with a more pronounced maximum. The effect in solid methane is a typical co-operative phenomenon as are also the order–disorder anomaly in $\beta$-brass and that of ferromagnetic substances in the neighbourhood of the Curie point. They may all be regarded as examples of phase transformations of the second order. In these cases, owing to the presence of a strong interaction, the jumping of one atom or group of atoms to another energy state increases the probability that another jump will occur. It was previously supposed by Pauling and others that the solid methane anomaly was due to the molecules at lower temperatures performing angular oscillations and then at the 'λ-point' passing over into free rotation in the crystal. It is, however, now believed that the effect is due to the methane molecules vibrating about some equilibrium position determined by the electrostatic field of the crystal lattice and periodically 'flipping' to an equivalent position connected with the earlier one by some symmetry operation consistent with the type of lattice present. Above the 'λ-point' there is a random distribution of all equivalent positions, but below it an increasing degree of order.

At helium temperatures the metals show marked deviations from the $T^3$ law; for example, the specific heat of copper is well represented by the expression

$$C_v = a(T/\theta_D)^3 + \gamma T \tag{9}$$

The first term gives the contribution from the lattice vibrations and the second term has been identified as the contribution to the specific heat of the conduction electrons. At high temperatures this linear term is quite negligibly small and the electronic specific heat can only be identified with certainty in the temperature region where the lattice specific heat, decreasing as $T^3$, has fallen to very low values. For copper the value of $\gamma$ is $0.688 \times 10^{-3}$ joules/gm. mol. deg.[2] (Corak, Garfunkel, Satterthwaite and Wexler 1955). The observed linear term was first explained by Sommerfeld. If the conduction electrons are treated as free particles, the classical theory predicts that the electronic specific heat will be $\frac{3}{2}k$ per electron independent of the temperature, a result completely at variance with the experimental facts. Sommerfeld treated the metal as a rectangular potential well in which the electrons are free to move and solved the Schrödinger equation for the problem to obtain the distribution of the electronic energy states. Then applying the Fermi-Dirac statistics instead of the classical Boltzmann statistics to the electrons the number of states lying between energies $\epsilon$ and $\epsilon + d\epsilon$ which are occupied is

$$dn = \frac{n(\epsilon)}{\exp\left[(\epsilon - \epsilon_F)/kT\right] + 1} d\epsilon = n(\epsilon)f(\epsilon)\,d\epsilon \tag{10}$$

where the Fermi energy $\epsilon_F$ is defined by

$$\int_0^\infty n(\epsilon)f(\epsilon)\,d\epsilon = n \tag{11}$$

where $n$ is the total number of electrons per unit volume.

The average energy per electron $\bar{\epsilon}$ is obtained from the total energy

$$n\bar{\epsilon} = \int_0^\infty \epsilon n(\epsilon)f(\epsilon)\,d\epsilon \tag{12}$$

Sommerfeld showed that for free electrons in a rectangular potential well

$$n(\epsilon)\,d\epsilon = 4\pi \cdot \frac{(2m)^{3/2}}{h^3}\,\epsilon^{1/2}\,d\epsilon$$

When this is inserted into (12) and the expression differentiated with respect to the temperature the electronic specific heat is found to be

$$C_e = \frac{4\pi^2}{3h^2}k^2 V\left(\frac{3N}{\pi V}\right)^{1/3} mT$$

$$= 3\cdot26 \times 10^{-5}\,V^{2/3}\,N_a^{1/3}\,T\,\text{cal./gm. mol. deg.} \tag{13}$$

where $V$ is the atomic volume and $N_a$ is the number of conduction electrons per atom. For copper the calculated value of $\gamma$ from (13) is $0\cdot502 \times 10^{-3}$ joules/gm. mol. deg.$^2$, of the same order of magnitude as the experimental value.

Equation (10) shows that at $0°$ K. all the electronic states are occupied up to the Fermi energy $\epsilon_F$ of $7\cdot04$ eV.† for copper. At any temperature above absolute zero some of the states immediately below

† Expressing $\epsilon_F$ as $kT_F$, $T_F$ for copper is 82,000 deg.

$\epsilon_F$ are empty and some of those immediately above $\epsilon_F$ are occupied but the spread is small compared with the total energy range and changes but little with the temperature at any temperature which would normally be considered as low. This picture is in striking contrast to the energy distribution based on classical ideas and explains the very small electronic contribution to the total specific heat of a metal.

If the Sommerfeld assumption that the conduction electrons move in a region of constant potential is replaced by the more adequate one that they are subject to a potential which is periodic with the periodicity of the crystal lattice, the band theory of solids results (see Chapter V). The only modification as regards the electronic specific heat is that the electrons now behave as if they have an effective mass $m^*$ in place of the free electron mass $m$. Equation (13) then becomes $C_e = (m^*/m)\gamma T$. The degree to which the electrons can be regarded as 'free' is given by the value of $m^*/m$ if the ratio $\gamma(\text{expt.})/\gamma(\text{free}$ electron is equated to $m^*/m$. For the monovalent metals (Na, K, Cu, Ag, Au) in which the conduction band is half-filled the free electron model should be a reasonable approximation to reality. That this is so is shown by the following values of $m^*/m$: Na 1·22; K 1·1; Cu 1·37; Ag 0·95; Au 1·16 (Parkinson).

The theoretical prediction of $m^*/m$ for metals in the other columns of the periodic table and in particular the transition elements in which $m^*/m$ may become very large [Ni: $m^*/m = 28$] is beyond the scope of this book.

The electronic specific heat of those metals which become super-conducting at low temperatures shows other interesting features. These are discussed in Chapter V.

## CHAPTER V

# Electrical Conductivity

The variation with temperature of the electrical conductivity of the metallic elements, of alloys and of compounds has been the subject of very many investigations. The results show that electrical conductors fall naturally into the following groups;

(1) The majority of pure metals, intermetallic compounds and certain alloys for which the specific resistance is approximately proportional to the absolute temperature at temperatures down to about $\theta_D$. At lower temperatures there is a region where the specific resistance is proportional to the fifth power of the absolute temperature. Finally, at very low temperatures the resistance becomes almost independent of temperature.

(2) Certain other alloys such as eureka and manganin, for which the specific resistance is nearly independent of the temperature at about room temperature.

(3) The semiconductors, such as cuprous oxide, $Cu_2O$, silver sulphide, $Ag_2S$, germanium doped with traces of arsenic and silicon doped with traces of boron, for which the specific resistance is greater than that of pure metals and increases with decrease in temperature.

(4) The superconductors, in which all trace of electrical resistance disappears below a certain characteristic temperature.

The general form of the specific resistance–temperature curve for the pure metals, which crystallize in the cubic system, is shown in Fig. 23 in which the abscissae represent $r = \rho/\rho_0$ the specific resistance at temperature $T$ divided by that at $0°$ C. At not too low temperatures $(T > \theta_D)$ the specific resistance decreases somewhat more rapidly than is given by $\rho \propto T$. At very low temperatures the specific resistance of all 'pure' metals tends to become independent of the temperature as shown in Figs. 23 and 24. The various curves in the latter figure show the variation of the specific resistance of highly purified samples of any typical metal of different degrees of chemical purity or physical perfection. All the samples have a certain residual resistance (the resistance obtained by extrapolating the curve to absolute zero), this residual resistance being greater the greater the amount of impurity present in the sample and being also greater if strains and dislocations are present in the crystal lattice. The course of the resistance–temperature curve for an ideal strain-free metal can be deduced from the Matthiessen-Nernst rule

$$r = (r_{obs} - c)/(1 - c)$$

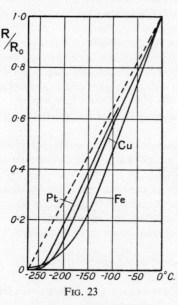

FIG. 23

where $r = \rho/\rho_0$ for the ideal metal and $c$ is a constant. The lowest curve of Fig. 24 shows the agreement among the values of $r$ obtained by means of the above formula from the observations on various samples. For the observations to have any value the amount of impurity present should not exceed $10^{-2}$–$10^{-4}$ per cent. In view of this only observations made with this fact in mind can be considered. The measurements of Meissner on gold, copper and lead from 273–4·2° K. may be mentioned, as they agree well with Grüneisen's empirical formula (see p. 94). The work of de Haas and van den Berg in the temperature range 20·4–1·4 °K. was designed to test the validity of the formula $\rho/\rho_0 = AT^B$ and derive the value of $B$. Several theories, including that of Bloch mentioned later, lead to such an expression when the temperature is less than $\theta_D/10$, where $\theta_D$ is the Debye temperature of the metal. Thus the observations on silver, white tin,† lead† and cadmium fit the formula with $B$ equal to 4·1, 4·3, 5·0 and 4·5 respectively. It was not possible to fit the observations

† Down to 3·7° K. (white tin) and 7·2° K. (lead) at which these metals become superconducting.

on platinum, copper or thallium with any single power of the temperature.

The behaviour of various samples of very pure gold was similar to that of silver at not too low temperatures. As the temperature was lowered still further, the curious phenomenon of a shallow minimum

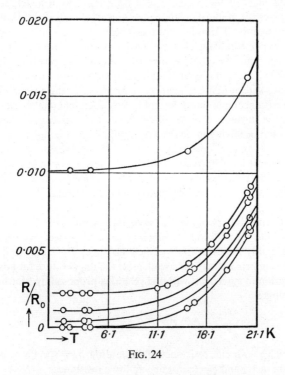

FIG. 24

in the resistance was observed by de Haas, de Boer and van den Berg. The temperature of the minimum varied with the value of the minimum resistance observed, being greater the greater $\rho_{min}/\rho_0$, $T_{min}$ varying from 6·95° K. to 3·7° K. for the samples used. The observations have been extended to 0·06° K. by Mendoza and Thomas; for one sample of gold $R/R_0$ varied from 152·8 at the temperature of the minimum, about 5° K., to 157·5 at 0·06° K. Many suggestions have been put forward to explain the resistance minimum such as: (1) some at present unknown factor of a fundamental nature which should be included in the theory of electrical resistance of metals; (2) some effect of the crystal boundaries; (3) a semiconductor type of temperature variation of resistance sets in at the lowest temperatures; (4) the effect of the presence of a transition group metal, such as manganese, as impurity with the incomplete $d$-shell slightly higher in energy than the Fermi level of the $s$-electrons of the metal, resulting in a temperature dependent scattering of the electrons of the metal into the empty $d$-shell. Later investigations of the electrical resistance of copper, silver and gold containing small amounts of Mn, Fe, Ni, Co have shown that explanation (4) is probably the correct one for the resistance minimum in gold containing minute amounts of impurity. In some of these dilute alloys in addition to a resistance minimum occurring in or near the liquid helium temperature range there is also a resistance maximum at still lower temperatures.

The variation with temperature of the specific resistance of dilute alloys, the constituents of which are completely miscible in one another, may be illustrated from the data of Clay on gold–silver alloys (Table 8).

The general shape of the $r$. $T$ curves is the same as that for the 'pure' metals, but the addition of a small amount of the second constituent considerably increases the specific resistance. This additional resistance is approximately independent of the temperature for any concentration in agreement with the relations proposed by Matthiessen and Vogt:

$$\rho = \rho_m + \xi, \quad \frac{d\rho}{dT} = \frac{d\rho_m}{dT} \tag{1}$$

in which $\rho =$ specific resistance of dilute alloy, $\rho_m =$ specific resistance of pure metal and $\xi =$ (constant) additive resistance.

It will be seen from column 6, Table 8, that the additional resistance is approximately proportional to the amount of silver present.

The electrical resistance of certain other alloys such as manganin and eureka, on the other hand, shows a very different temperature variation from that of the pure metals. Thus these alloys possess a very small negative coefficient of change of resistance at higher temperatures. As the temperature is lowered the resistance reaches a maximum and then decreases approximately linearly at low temperatures, below 100° K. for manganin as can be seen from Table 9.

The values also given in Table 9 for phosphor-bronze refer to one particular specimen of unannealed wire measured by Keesom and

TABLE 8

Specific Resistance of Au–Ag Alloys

| Vol. per cent Ag | Temp. °C. | $\rho_{obs} \times 10^9$ | $\rho_m \times 10^9$ | $\xi \times 10^9$ | $\xi$ per 1 vol. per cent Ag |
|---|---|---|---|---|---|
| 0.872 | 0 | 2416 | 2136 | 280 | |
| | − 103·83 | 1570 | 1266 | 304 | 361 |
| | − 182·73 | 916 | 580 | 335 | |
| | − 252·92 | 359 | 17 | 341 | |
| 0.960 | 0 | 2444 | 2136 | 308 | |
| | − 103·83 | 1596 | 1266 | 329 | 353 |
| | − 182·73 | 940 | 580 | 360 | |
| | − 252·92 | 380 | 17 | 363 | |
| 1.586 | 0 | | | | |
| | − 103·83 | 2637 | 2130 | 506 | |
| | − 182·73 | 1806 | 1263 | 543 | 350 |
| | − 252·92 | 1161 | 578 | 582 | |
| | | 606 | 17 | 588 | |

van den Ende, for one value of the measuring current and in the absence of any magnetic field. It has since been shown that the variation of resistance which only occurs below 7° K. is due to the presence of a small amount of lead, present as inclusions with a large variation in size. These inclusions become superconducting over a wide range in temperature because of the large variation in size. The mechanism of the temperature variation of resistance also accounts for the great sensitivity of leaded phosphor-bronze to current density and external magnetic field. Annealing the wire by heating to red heat completely destroys the temperature variation of the resistance. As mentioned in Chapter II this material can be used, under appropriate conditions as a resistance thermometer for temperatures below 7° K.

In the semiconductors, both of the intrinsic type in extremely pure material and of the extrinsic or impurity type where the conductivity

TABLE 9

| Manganin Cu, 84 per cent; Mn, 12 per cent; Ni, 4 per cent (Onnes and Holst) | | Phosphor bronze (unannealed) Keesom and v.d. Ende | |
|---|---|---|---|
| $t°$ C. | R (ohms) | $T°$ K. | r |
| 16·5 | 124·20 | 4·237 | 0·7725 |
| − 183·0 | 119·35 | 3·581 | 0·7439 |
| − 201·7 | 117·90 | 2·916 | 0·7156 |
| − 253·3 | 113·42 | 2·396 | 0·6944 |
| − 258·0 | 112·91 | 1·823 | 0·6728 |
| − 269·0 | 111·92 | 1·507 | 0·6625 |
| − 271·5 | 111·71 | 1·257 | 0·6536 |

is due to the presence of small amounts of certain impurities, the specific resistance increases exponentially with decrease in temperature, $\rho = \rho_0 e^{A/T}$.

A semi-empirical formula, which reproduces the specific resistance of pure metals reasonably well over a wide temperature range, has been given by Grüneisen in the form

$$\rho = C \left\{ \frac{20}{x^5} \int_0^x \frac{\xi^4 d\xi}{e^\xi - 1} - \frac{4}{e^x - 1} \right\} \qquad (2)$$

in which $C$ is a constant for any given metal,

$$\xi = h\nu/kT, \quad x = \theta_D/T = h\nu_m/kT$$

$\theta_D =$ Debye characteristic temperature. The value of $\theta_D$ deduced from (2) agrees reasonably well with that obtained by fitting equation (6) of Chapter IV to the observed specific heat of the same metal. Blackman has pointed out that this calls for further investigation since in the theory of the electrical resistance of metals only the longitudinal vibrations of the lattice play a part in determining the resistance. The theoretical value of $\theta_D$ calculated for the longitudinal vibrations only is, however, quite different from that calculated for both longitudinal and transverse vibrations as in the Debye theory.

For very high temperatures (2) reduces to $\rho = C(T/\theta_D)$ and for low temperatures to $\rho = 497 \cdot 7 C(T/\theta_D)^5$. The Grüneisen formula thus leads to the same rate of variation of the resistance with temperature at high and low temperatures as the theory of Bloch now to be discussed.

At the beginning of this century a classical theory was put forward by Drude and later amplified by Lorentz to explain the electrical conductivity of metals. Free electrons were assumed to be present in the metal and were treated as an electron gas in calculating the drift velocity acquired by them from an applied electric field. This led to the following formula for the specific resistance:

$$\rho = \frac{mv}{nel} \tag{3}$$

where $m =$ mass of electron, $v =$ average velocity of electrons, $n =$ number of electrons per unit volume and $l =$ mean free path of electron. $v$ was determined by equating the kinetic energy of an electron to $(\frac{3}{2})kT$. The thermal conductivity of the metal was also calculated on the assumption that the heat was conducted by the electron gas. The two immediate successes of the theory were the reproduction of Ohm's law and Wiedemann and Franz's law (the ratio of the thermal to electrical conductivity of metals is proportional to the absolute temperature, the constant of proportionality being approximately the same for all metals). However the theory proved unsatisfactory when an attempt was made to reproduce the observed electrical conductivity and its variation with temperature by means of equation (3). An unrealistic assumption had to be made with regard to $n$ and $l$. Again, equating the energy of an electron to $(\frac{3}{2})kT$ involved the existence of an electronic specific heat of $(\frac{3}{2})k$ per electron, quite contrary to the observed facts.

In 1928 Sommerfeld treated the electrons as free particles moving in a region of constant electrical potential and obeying the Fermi statistics. As mentioned on p. 88 this removes the difficulty of the electronic specific heat. Formula (3) still holds but now $v$ is $v_F$ the average velocity of an electron with the Fermi energy $\epsilon_F$ and is therefore of the order of $10^8$ cm./sec. and nearly independent of the temperature. The number of electrons per unit volume $n$ can reasonably be taken to be constant and equal to the number of valency electrons per unit volume. The temperature variation of the resistance must then be due principally to the variation of the mean free path $l$ with temperature. To reproduce the observed values of the resistance of pure metals $l$ must then be about one hundred times the interatomic distance at room temperature and still larger at low temperatures. Since neither the theory of Drude nor of Sommerfeld provides any means of calculating the magnitude of the mean free path, the very large values of $l$ remained a mystery until the advent of Bloch's theory.

This theory has provided an understanding of many features of the physical properties of solids. To calculate the possible flow of electrons through the crystal lattice of a solid the interaction of an electron with the ions of the lattice is taken into account by assuming the electron to be moving in an electrostatic field which is periodic with the periodicity of the lattice. The results of the calculation may be illustrated by considering the case of a one-dimensional lattice. The wave function is then of the form

$$\psi(x) = u_k(x)\,e^{\pm ikx}$$

where $u_k(x)$ has the period of the lattice so that $u_k(x+a) = u_k(x)$ and $a$ is the lattice spacing. The wave number $k$ is equal to $2\pi/\lambda$.

It is then found that the energy values possible for an electron moving through the crystal form a series of continuous *bands* of states separated from each other by finite intervals of forbidden states.

The curve of the energy states of a 'free' electron plotted as a function of the wave number $k$ is a parabola. Comparing this with the energy curves of an electron in a periodic field it is seen that in the latter case discontinuities occur along the parabola at values of $k$ given by

$$ka = n\pi; \quad n = \pm 1, \pm 2, \pm 3, \ldots$$

The $\epsilon$, $k$ graph is divided into a series of zones, known as Brillouin zones, at the boundary of which there is a discontinuous increase in the energy. The first zone stretches from $k = \pi/a$ to $k = -\pi/a$, the second includes the segments $\pi/a < k < 2\pi/a$ and $-2\pi/a < k < -\pi/a$.

In three dimensions the wave vector $\mathbf{k}$ determines the boundaries of the Brillouin zones, the values of $\mathbf{k}_x$, $\mathbf{k}_y$ and $\mathbf{k}_z$ being subject to conditions similar to $\mathbf{k}$. The shape of the surface so obtained depends on the crystalline symmetry of the lattice. Thus for the simple cubic lattice the first Brillouin zone is bounded by a cube, the second by a dodecahedron. In the body-centred cubic lattice the first zone is a dodecahedron and in the face-centred cubic lattice it is a truncated octahedron. It is characteristic of the Brillouin zones that the moving electrons are reflected at the boundaries of the zones. The condition for $\mathbf{k}$ quoted above is equivalent to the Bragg equation for the reflection of X-rays at certain crystal planes.

The position of the constant energy surfaces in $\mathbf{k}$ space relative to the boundary of the first Brillouin zone is important for the understanding of many of the physical properties of metals and alloys.

Each energy band contains $N$ wave functions ($N =$ number of atoms in the solid) each of which can be occupied by two electrons of opposite spin. For a net current to be produced electrons must be scattered into vacant states as the interchange of electrons between two occupied states does not result in a net current. This also limits the electrons taking part in current flow to those with energies close to the Fermi energy and only a small proportion of the valency electrons function as 'conduction electrons'.

In the band theory the motion of an electron is derived from the same expressions as in the 'free electron' case but with an effective mass $m^*$ in place of the real mass $m$. The variation of $m^*$ within a band has several remarkable features. In the lower half of the band the effective mass is positive rising to infinity at the centre of the band. In the upper half of the band $m^*$ is negative. Only when $m^*/m$ is nearly equal to 1 does the electron behave approximately like a free electron.

7

The band theory gives an immediate distinction between an insulator and a conductor such as a metal. If the lowest band in a solid is completely filled with electrons and all the higher bands are empty and if the gap between the lowest and the next higher band is large compared with $kT$, then the solid is an insulator. On the other hand, if the band is only partly filled the solid is a metal. If the gap width is small in the first case, say 1 eV., it is possible for electrons to be thermally excited from the full band into the next empty one at not too low temperatures. The solid then behaves as an intrinsic semiconductor.

In the case of the alkali metals and of copper, silver and gold where there is one valency electron per atom, the lowest band is half filled and the solid should be a good conductor as is indeed the case. On the other hand, in the case of beryllium with 2 valency electrons the lowest band will be completely full on the one dimensional model. It would therefore be expected that this element would be an insulator whereas it is a metal though with a lower conductivity than lithium. This conclusion, however, does not hold when the three-dimensional case is considered for then there is a possibility of overlap in the energy bands. So in beryllium the $s$ band contains somewhat less than two electrons per atom and overlaps the $p$ band where the remaining electrons are to be found. The element is thus a metal as actually observed.

To obtain the resistivity of a metal on Bloch's theory the passage of electron waves through the crystal lattice must be calculated. It was then found that the electrons are not scattered by a perfectly periodic lattice and such a structure would exhibit no electrical resistance. The electron waves are only scattered by the departures from perfection in the lattice. These may be impurity atoms, vacancies or dislocations and this kind of imperfection produces a scattering and hence an electrical resistance which is independent of the temperature (residual resistance). Scattering of the electron waves is also produced by the displacement of the ions from their equilibrium positions by thermal agitation. This scattering is temperature-dependent and produces the 'ideal resistance' of the metal vanishing at absolute zero (see lowest curve in Fig. 24).

The scattering by displaced ions on the lattice may be regarded as an electron–phonon interaction where the phonon is a quantum of vibrational energy of the lattice. The incident electron may absorb or emit a phonon. Momentum is conserved within the electron–phonon system according to the relation

$$\mathbf{k}' = \mathbf{k} \pm \mathbf{q}$$

or we have a process in which

$$\mathbf{k}' = \mathbf{k} \pm \mathbf{q} + 2\pi\mathbf{b}$$

where $\mathbf{k}$ is the wave vector of the incident electron, $\mathbf{k}'$ that of the scattered electron, $\mathbf{q}$ the wave vector of the elastic wave in the lattice, $\mathbf{b}$ is a vector in reciprocal space (for the simple cubic lattice

$$2\pi\mathbf{b} = 2\pi\mathbf{n}/a$$

where $\mathbf{n}$ is a vector with integral components and $a$ is the lattice spacing). In the second case, where the transition is known as an 'umklapp process', the electron wave emits or absorbs a phonon and is reflected at the boundary of the Brillouin zone.

In these processes the energy of an electron near the Fermi level (of the order of several electron volts) is not changed much as the most energetic phonon has an energy of only about 0·01 eV., but the electron can be scattered through large angles when $\mathbf{k} \simeq \mathbf{q}$. At high temperatures scattering may take place over a wide range of angles and the calculated variation of resistivity with temperature is $\rho \propto T$. At low temperatures on the other hand only low energy phonons are present and electrons near the Fermi level are only scattered through small angles. Using the Debye theory to calculate the phonon distribution leads to the result $\rho \propto T^5$ at temperatures low compared with $\theta_D$.

Bloch's theory gives a good qualitative account of many of the properties of metals but an exact quantitative agreement is not to be expected in view of the many approximations made in the calculation. Agreement with experiment is most nearly obtained in the alkali metals which approximate most closely to the 'free electron model'. A repetition of the theory using more complicated but more exact mathematical methods has not greatly improved the situation. It became apparent that it was necessary to investigate the effect of various circumstances which had not, for the sake of simplicity, been taken into account in the Bloch theory. Two such effects are correlation effects and phonon drag.

In the Bloch theory no account is taken of the Coulomb repulsion between the electrons. This is unsatisfactory as the repulsive forces are quite strong and influence the motion of the electrons so as to keep them from approaching each other too closely, the so-called correlation effect. This has been studied in plasma theory particularly by Bohm and Pines. The Coulomb repulsion ensures that each electron is surrounded by a denuded region which, because of the positive charge of the lattice ions, has on the average a positive charge. The moving particles now consist of the electrons together with the denuded region around each one and are effectively neutral. There will now be no long range Coulomb forces between the particles and the latter can be regarded as moving independently. This removes several deficiencies of the simple Bloch theory but retains the concepts of Fermi surface and Brillouin zone.

In the simple Bloch theory it is tacitly assumed that the equilibrium of the phonons is unaffected by the electrical and thermal currents through the metal. There is, however, a complicated interaction between electrical and thermal currents carried by the phonons. This leads to a 'drag' of the electrons by the phonon current created by a temperature gradient. Thus in the steady state as distinct from the equilibrium state corrections to the electrical and thermal conductivity and to the thermoelectric properties result from this phonon drag. The thermoelectric properties are the most affected and the amended theory is more nearly in agreement with the very complicated phenomena observed at the lowest temperatures. Much work, experimental and theoretical, will be needed before the picture of the electrical and thermal properties of metals at low temperatures can be regarded as wholly satisfactory.

## Superconductivity

When measuring the electrical resistance of very pure mercury at helium temperatures Kamerlingh Onnes found in 1911 that just below the temperature of the boiling-point of helium the resistance began to fall rapidly, and that when the temperature had fallen another $\frac{1}{20}$ of a degree all measurable resistance had disappeared. This new property, zero resistance at a finite temperature, was given the name superconductivity. This property has since been found in a number of pure metals, alloys and compounds. In the case of an absolutely pure strain-free metal in the form of a single crystal the transition from normal conductivity to superconductivity is probably discontinuous. The smallest transition interval observed by de Haas and Voogd for a single crystal of tin was $\frac{1}{1000}$ degree but the interval increases with increasing number of crystals present in the wire (Fig. 25), increasing chemical impurity, etc. In the case of alloys the transition interval may be one degree or more. The pure metals which

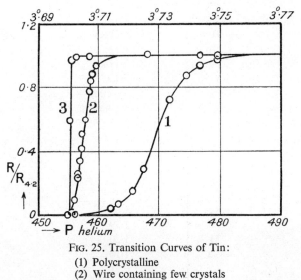

FIG. 25. Transition Curves of Tin:
(1) Polycrystalline
(2) Wire containing few crystals
(3) Single crystal

have so far been found to show superconductivity are to be found in Table 10, together with their observed transition points.† Almost all the other metals have been tested for superconductivity down to $1 \cdot 1 – 1 \cdot 4°$ K. and in many cases down to $0 \cdot 05 – 0 \cdot 09°$ K.

In addition to the metals quoted in Table 10 which have been examined in bulk, bismuth, iron and beryllium in the form of films of a thickness not greater than $10^{-5}$ cm. deposited on a solid surface

† The transition point is usually defined as the temperature at which half the resistance present before the transition has disappeared.

at $4°$ K. also exhibit superconductivity, the transition temperatures for Bi and Be being about $6°$ K. and $8°$ K. respectively. These films are probably in the amorphous state.

TABLE 10

| Metal | Transition temperature |
|-------|------------------------|
| Tc | $11 \cdot 2°$ K. |
| Nb | $9 \cdot 22$ |
| Pb | $7 \cdot 175$ |
| V | $5 \cdot 1$ |
| La | $\begin{cases} 5 \cdot 9 \text{ cubic} \\ 4 \cdot 8 \text{ hexag.} \end{cases}$ |
| Ta | $4 \cdot 4$ |
| Hg | $\begin{cases} 4 \cdot 153 \ (\alpha) \\ 3 \cdot 94 \quad (\beta) \end{cases}$ |
| Sm | $3 \cdot 73$ |
| In | $3 \cdot 37$ |
| Tl | $2 \cdot 38$ |
| Re | $1 \cdot 699$ |
| Th | $1 \cdot 39$ |
| Al | $1 \cdot 20$ |
| Ga | $1 \cdot 10$ |
| Zn | $0 \cdot 91$ |
| U | $0 \cdot 8$ |
| Os | $0 \cdot 71$ |
| Zr | $0 \cdot 70$ |
| Cd | $0 \cdot 56$ |
| Ru | $0 \cdot 47$ |
| Ti | $0 \cdot 387$ |

Superconductivity is also influenced by the crystalline structure of the metal. Thus the transition temperatures of cubic and hexagonal close-packed lanthanum are $5 \cdot 9°$ K. and $4 \cdot 8°$ K. respectively and those of $\alpha$- and $\beta$-mercury 4·153° K. and 3·94° K. The modification of bismuth stable at low temperatures and one atmosphere pressure is not superconducting but the crystalline form produced by increasing the pressure to 20,000–40,000 atm. becomes superconducting at 7° K. White tin (tetragonal) has a transition temperature of 3·73° K., but grey tin (cubic) is not a superconductor.

Since it has become possible to examine the properties of the separated isotopes of various superconductors, it has been found that the transition temperature varies among the various isotopes of any one metal approximately or accurately according to the relation $T_c = kM^{-1/2}$, where $M$ is the atomic mass of the isotope. Thus for mercury $T_c$ varies from 4·185° K., for $M = 199·5$, to 4·146° K., for $M = 203·4$.

Superconductivity is not found among the monovalent elements nor among the ferromagnetic† and antiferromagnetic elements.

With regard to binary alloys it may be stated that superconductivity occurs in (i) alloys of two superconductors, (ii) alloys of one super-conductor and one non-superconductor in which the crystal lattice of the superconductor is preserved, and (iii) in certain intermetallic compounds. Case (iii) is interesting as it includes examples such as $Au_2Bi$, LiBi, NiBi which become superconducting although the separate components are not superconductors.

Superconductivity has also been observed in a number of hydrides, borides, carbides, nitrides, silicides and sulphides. All these substances have a metallic appearance but their electrical properties at higher temperatures are rather those of semiconductors. CuS becomes superconducting at 1·6° K., NbC at 10·1–10·5° K., NbH at 7–13° K., NbN at 15–16° K. (the non-metallic component may be present in amounts both greater and less than that corresponding to the above formula giving rise to the quoted spread in the transition tempera-ture). The substance $Nb_3Sn$, for which $T_c = 18°$ K., has the highest transition temperature yet observed.

If a current is flowing in a circuit containing a resistance $R$ and an inductance $L$ and the e.m.f. is suddenly removed, the current falls to $1/e$ of its original value in a time $t$ equal to $L/R$. With normal con-ductors $t$ is of the order of $10^{-5}$ sec. Since the earliest determinations had shown that the electrical resistance of a superconductor, even if

† Certain ferromagnetic alloys do, however, show superconductivity.

not strictly zero, could not be greater than $10^{-10} \times R_{0° C.}$, $t$ for a super-conductor must be at least of the order of many hours and a current will persist long after the e.m.f. has been removed. Such persistent currents were detected by Onnes in his early experiments and later used by Onnes and Tuyn to set an upper limit to the possible micro-residual resistance of a superconductor. A dynamometer was con-

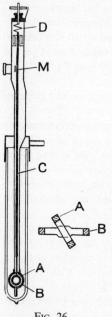

structed consisting of two circular lead rings, the outer one B fixed and the inner one A suspended from a torsion-head by means of a spring and glass rod as shown in Fig. 26. The rings were immersed in liquid helium in the Dewar vessel and the latter was placed between the poles of an electromagnet so that the plane of the rings was perpendicular to the direction of the magnetic field. The latter was greater than the critical field strength for lead at 4·2° K. (see later). The field was then reduced to zero and a per-sistent current induced in the lead rings, which was calculated to be 370 and 170 amperes for the outer and inner rings re-spectively. The torsion head was then turned so that the plane of the inner ring made an angle of 30° with that of the outer ring. The angle through which the torsion head had to be turned was greater than 30° on account of the couple due to the action of the currents tending to keep the rings coplanar. By means of the mirror M it was possible to observe any change in the angle between the

Fig. 26

rings, resulting from a decrease in the current strengths. It was found that the currents did not decrease by as much as 1 part in 40,000 per hour. A calculation of the time of relaxation $t$ then showed that any resistance present in the lead at 4·2° K. was less than $10^{-12} \times R_{0° C.}$. Later repetitions of the experiment with greater sensitivity reduced the residual resistance to less than $10^{-17} \times R_{0° C.}$. In an experiment carried out by Collins at M.I.T. a persistent current has been observed over a period of several years. It may therefore be concluded that a superconductor is characterized by the complete absence of electrical resistance.

Soon after the discovery of superconductivity it was found by Onnes that if a superconductor is placed in a magnetic field and the strength of the latter is gradually increased the normal resistance of the wire suddenly begins to return at a definite value of the field strength. The resistance increases with increasing field until the whole of the normal resistance corresponding to the temperature of the experiment has returned. Fig. 27 illustrates the phenomenon for a long cylindrical wire (polycrystalline or single crystal) of tin in a

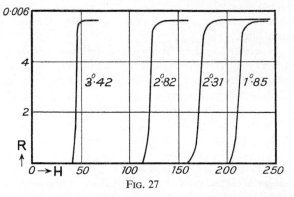

Fig. 27

uniform longitudinal magnetic field. The critical magnetic field $H_c$ is defined as the field required to restore half the resistance corresponding to the temperature $T$ in the non-superconducting state. For the soft metals and for pure compounds $H_c$ is of the order of a few tens to a few hundreds of oersteds, that for the hard metals such as niobium, vanadium and tantalum rises to 1000–2000 oe. but is greatly dependent on the ultimate purity of the sample. With certain alloys the critical field defined as above is much larger; thus for the alloy of lead and bismuth containing 35 at. per cent of bismuth, $H_c = 18,450$ oe. at $4.22°$ K. and 25,700 oe. at $1.97°$ K. In a number of cases $H_c$ is related to the temperature by the formula

$$H_c = H_0(1 - (T/T_c)^2)$$

where $H_0$ is the critical field at $0°$ K. and $T_c$ is the normal transition temperature in the absence of any magnetic field, though this parabolic formula is only a rough approximation in some cases. The curve may conveniently be regarded as a boundary curve on a phase diagram separating the regions where the substance is superconducting, *s* (below the curve) from those where it is normal *n* (above the curve), the more so as it has been shown that for a pure strain-free specimen the transition $n \rightarrow s$ is reversible (see later).

The return of the resistance of a long cylindrical *single* crystal wire in a transverse magnetic field takes place quite differently. In this case, the first traces of resistance appear when the applied field is $H_c/2$ and then the resistance rises approximately linearly until it has returned completely at approximately the same field strength as in the longitudinal case. The significance of this difference in behaviour will be discussed later.

It was further found by Onnes that if the density of the current through a cylindrical superconducting wire is raised above a certain critical value the normal resistance reappears. Silsbee suggested, and it was later established experimentally for soft superconductors, that the critical value of the current is that current which produces the critical value of the magnetic field at the surface of the conductor. The effect of the current, is thus not a fresh phenomenon in itself.

## Magnetic Properties of Superconductors

The magnetic properties of superconductors are quite as remarkable as their electrical properties. The incentive to investigate them in detail was provided when von Laue put forward an explanation for the fact that the magnetic field at which normal resistance begins to be restored in a monocrystalline cylinder in a transverse field is approximately half that in a longitudinal field.

Since the electrical resistance of a superconductor is zero no electrical field $E$ can exist in the metal and so from Maxwell's equation $c \operatorname{curl} E = -\dot{B}$, the magnetic induction $B$ of the superconductor cannot vary with the time. If now we have a superconducting cylinder at a temperature $T$ ($T < T_c$) and apply a transverse magnetic field less than the critical field at that temperature since $B$ was initially zero in the absence of a magnetic field it must remain zero after the field has been applied. The lines of force of the field are constrained to avoid the superconducting cylinder and so crowd together most at the opposite ends of the transverse diameter of the cylinder. Calculation of the distribution of the magnetic field in this case shows that the field strength immediately outside the cylinder at the ends of transverse diameter is exactly twice as great as its value at a large distance away where it is undisturbed by the presence of the cylinder. Thus we might expect superconductivity to be destroyed along the sides of the wire when the applied field is $H_c/2$. Then as the field strength is increased, the magnetic field might penetrate more and more into the cylinder until finally the whole of the latter is in the normal state.

The situation is quite different for the case of the cylinder in a uniform longitudinal magnetic field. The presence of the cylinder does not disturb the uniformity of the field and the latter reaches its critical value $H_c$ simultaneously over the whole surface of the cylinder, giving a sharp transition from the superconducting to the normal state.

The magnetic behaviour described above cannot be regarded as a complete explanation of the reappearance of normal resistance in de Haas and Voogd's experiments as the normal regions at the ends of the transverse diameter will be in parallel with the still superconducting remainder of the cylinder and so no potential difference will appear between the ends of the cylinder. The additional facts about the real distribution of the normal and superconducting regions required to complete the explanation were discovered much later. Nevertheless, the suggestion served to stimulate an interest in the magnetic properties of superconductors. These were established as a result of the researches of Meissner and Ochsenfeld in the first place and later of many other workers. Determinations were made of the magnetic field distribution around metal specimens by means of search coils or small bismuth wires, of the induction inside the specimen by means of a bismuth wire inside a disk-shaped cavity perpendicular to the applied field, of the total induction in the specimen by withdrawing the latter from a coil connected to a ballistic galvanometer and of the intensity of magnetization by measuring the force exerted on the specimen (usually a sphere) by a non-homogeneous field. All the methods led to the same picture of the magnetic properties of the superconductor. Thus with a cylindrical specimen maintained at a constant temperature lower than $T_c$ in a longitudinal magnetic field which is increased from zero to a value greater than $H_c$ the magnetic field fails to penetrate the cylinder $(B=0)$ until the critical field strength is reached, after which the metal is in the normal conducting state and $B = H$ (the susceptibility of the metal in its normal state may be taken to be zero, actually of the order of $10^{-7}$). If the magnetic field is then reduced to zero, the magnetic phenomena are found to be reversible.† Again, when a constant longitudinal magnetic field is applied at some relatively high temperature and then the temperature is lowered so that the specimen becomes superconducting, the magnetic field is found to be ejected from the metal and again $B = 0$. This process again takes place reversibly. The first case (temperature constant) could have been predicted from Maxwell's equation for a metal with zero resistance, but the second case (magnetic field constant) could not. It is something new and characteristic of superconductivity. Summarizing, we can say that an ideally pure superconductor in a magnetic field less than the critical field is characterized by a magnetic induction $B$ which is zero throughout the specimen,‡ or by a volume susceptibility

$$K = -\frac{1}{4\pi}$$

so that a superconductor is a perfect diamagnetic substance. An alternative description is that when a metal becomes superconducting in a magnetic field, persistent currents are set up at the surface of the specimen with such a strength and distribution as to maintain $B = 0$ throughout the specimen.

The above description has been restricted to the case of a long cylinder in a longitudinal magnetic field. If the field is transverse (or in any other shaped specimen in which the critical field strength is not reached simultaneously throughout the whole specimen), other phenomena occur. For the case of the solid cylinder maintained at constant temperature in a transverse magnetic field which is increased from zero to $H > H_c$, the observed phenomena are as follows: The maximum field outside the cylinder (at opposite ends of the transverse diameter) $H_{\max}$ is equal to $2H$ ($H$ = applied field) from $H = 0$ to

† The description of the phenomena given in this section is somewhat idealized to the case of an ideally pure single crystal. Thus the hysteresis and relaxation phenomena which occur to some extent in any actual specimen are ignored as they are believed to be of secondary origin and vary with the purity and physical state of the specimen.

‡ Strictly speaking $B = 0$, except in a very thin transition layer at the surface, now known to be about $10^{-5}$ cm. thick.

$H > H_c/2$, then $H_{max}$ remains constant at $H_{max} = H_c$ until $H$ has risen to $H_c$, finally $H_{max} = H$ for $H > H_c$. The magnetic induction $B$ inside the cylinder remains equal to zero from $H = 0$ to $H = H_c/2$, then rises linearly to $B = H$ as $H$ rises to $H_c$, and finally, $B = H$ for $H > H_c$. It is during the gradual rise of the magnetic induction that the normal resistance is gradually restored in the cylinder. The specimen is then said to be in the 'intermediate state', neither purely superconducting nor purely normal. Later theoretical investigations, particularly by Landau, showed that the measured induction must be an average value and not the local magnetic induction at any point in the specimen. In the intermediate state the cylinder splits up into a complicated mixture of superconducting and normal regions in which $B = 0$ and $B = H_c$ respectively. According to Landau in the neighbourhood of the axis of the cylinder the regions have the form of discs or slices parallel to the direction of the external field, but near the surface the regions may undergo a complicated branching process. The fraction $x$ of the specimen which is in the normal state is given by $x = B_{obs}/H_c$ and the thickness of the laminae is estimated to be about $1-5 \times 10^{-2}$ cm. Evidence of the general correctness of this view of the structure of the intermediate state was obtained by Shubnikov and Nakhutin, who showed that a sphere in the intermediate state is superconducting parallel to the direction of the applied field but has a normal resistance perpendicular to this direction. This structure also shows why resistance is observed in the cylinder in a transverse field as soon as the external field is greater than about $H_c/2$ and provides the missing step in von Laue's explanation. By moving a very small bismuth wire about in the disk-shaped cavity between two hemispheres and using it to measure the local magnetic field when the sphere is in the intermediate state, Meshkovsky and Shalnikov have obtained detailed evidence of the fine structure of the intermediate state. Though their results indicated the presence of a more complicated structure than that predicted theoretically the general picture was confirmed. More recently direct visual evidence of the distribution of normal and superconducting regions has been obtained by Schawlow using a powder method similar to the Bitter method of mapping the domain structure in ferromagnetic materials and by Alers using the Faraday effect in a thin layer of cerium nitrate.

It has also been shown that an electric current in a superconductor is always a surface current. Thus when a current is made to flow through a cylinder of metal at a temperature above its normal transition point by connecting it to a battery and external resistance, the current is uniformly distributed over the cross-section of the wire. If now the temperature is lowered so that the metal becomes superconducting, the current redistributes itself so as to flow only in the surface layer.

The magnetic properties described above are those of the pure metals (soft) and compounds. Alloy superconductors show a much more complicated behaviour. Thus the critical field required to destroy superconductivity is usually very large though a much smaller field will begin to penetrate into the superconducting alloy. The Meissner effect is never complete, and removal of a magnetic field results in an appreciable frozen-in magnetic moment. It is, however, beyond the scope of the present monograph to give a detailed account of the properties of superconducting alloys.

### Thermal Properties of Superconductors

Since it has been proved that the transition from the superconducting state to the normal state at constant temperature in a variable magnetic field, and at constant magnetic field and variable temperature is reversible, it is possible to apply classical thermodynamic principles to the case and deduce various relations between the thermal and magnetic properties. Thus we may treat the transition as an ordinary phase change (first order) and state that at any point on the boundary curve (critical field-temperature curve) the thermodynamic potentials $G_s$ and $G_n$ of the two phases in equilibrium along the curve are equal and that for any physical change taking place on the curve $\Delta G_s = \Delta G_n$. Writing the thermodynamic potential $G_s$ of the superconducting phase as $U_s - TS_s - H\sigma_s$ and a corresponding expression for $G_n$ in which $U_s =$ internal energy, $S_s =$ entropy, $\sigma_s =$ magnetization, all per gm. mol. and putting $\sigma_s = - VH/4\pi$ ($V =$ volume of gm. mol. of metal), $\sigma_n = 0$, it can be shown that for the case of the long cylinder in a longitudinal magnetic field

$$\frac{dH_c}{dT} = - \frac{4\pi(S_n - S_s)}{VH_c} \tag{4}$$

where $H_c =$ critical magnetic field at temperature $T$.

From (4) it follows that the heat absorbed in the transition $s \to n$ (latent heat $L$) at temperature $T$ is given by

$$L = T(S_n - S_s) = -\frac{VTH_c}{4\pi} \cdot \frac{dH_c}{dT} \tag{5}$$

There will also be a difference in the specific heat $C_s$ and $C_n$ of the superconducting and normal phases given by

$$C_n - C_s = T\frac{d}{dT}(S_n - S_s) = -\frac{VT}{4\pi}\left\{\left(\frac{dH_c}{dT}\right)^2 + H_c\frac{d^2 H_c}{dT^2}\right\} \tag{6}$$

It will be seen from (5) and (6) that for the transition $s \to n$ occurring at the normal transition point $T_c$ (i.e. in the absence of a magnetic field) no latent heat is absorbed, and there is a sudden jump in the specific heat

$$\Delta C = C_n - C_s = -\frac{VT_c}{4\pi}\left(\frac{dH_c}{dT}\right)^2_{T_c}$$

where $dH_c/dT$ is the slope of the critical field curve at $T_c$. Thus the transition in the absence of a magnetic field is an example of a second order transition though the transition is of the first order when a magnetic field is present.

It has been shown by Gorter and Casimir that when the specimen has a different shape and so passes through the intermediate state during the transition $s \to n$, the latent heat is absorbed gradually over a certain range of temperature (in a constant magnetic field) or over a certain range of field strength (at constant temperature), but the total latent heat is still given by formula (5).

These thermodynamical deductions have received complete confirmation from the calorimetric determinations of Keesom and many others and the complete reversibility of the transition for ideal superconductors has been established conclusively. A comparison of the calculated and experimental values of $\Delta C$ in the absence of a magnetic field is given in Table 11. The specific heat of a superconducting metal in the normal state below the transition point (i.e. in a magnetic field greater than $H_c$) obeys the law

$$C_n/V = \gamma T + b_n T^3$$

as in the case of a non-superconductor (see Chapter IV) and again the linear term represents the contribution due to the conduction electrons.

On the other hand the specific heat in the superconducting state varies with the temperature according to the relation

$$C_s/V = a\gamma T_c e^{-bT_c/T} + b_s T^3$$

The first term, the electronic specific heat, is compatible with a model in which the levels of the excited electrons are separated from the

TABLE 11

| Element | $T_c^\circ K.$ | $\dfrac{V}{cm^3/mole}$ | $(dH_c/dT)_{T_e}$ | $\Delta C$ calc. (cal./deg. mole) | $\Delta C$ obs. (cal./deg. mole) |
|---|---|---|---|---|---|
| Pb | 7·22 | 17·8 | 200 | $10 \times 10^{-3}$ | $12·6 \times 10^{-3}$ |
| Ta | 4·40 | 10·9 | 320 | 9·4 | 8·2; 9 |
| Sn | 3·73 | 16·1 | 151 | 2·61 | 2·4; 2·9 |
| In | 3·37 | 15·2 | 146 | 2·08 | 2·3 |
| Tl | 2·38 | 16·8 | 139 | 1·47 | 1·48 |
| Al | 1·20 | 9·9 | 177 | 0·71 | 0·46 |

ground state, the superconducting electrons, by an energy gap which has its maximum value at 0° K. and decreases to zero at $T_c$. This term appears in the Bardeen, Cooper and Schrieffer theory of superconductivity and the predicted value of the energy gap at 0° K. is $3·5\,kT_c$ in agreement with the data for the specific heat of superconductors and of infra-red absorption and ultrasonic attenuation as mentioned later.

It will be seen that the entropy of the normal state is greater than that of the superconducting state at the same temperature indicating that the superconducting phase has a greater degree of order.

The table also shows the smallness of the energy difference between the superconducting and normal states. The fact that the difference is very small compared with that occurring in a phase change of the first order adds to the difficulty of finding the actual mechanism for the $s \to n$ transition.

## Various Other Properties

A thermodynamic treatment of the transition from normal to superconductivity has shown that a number of physical properties of the material should change at the transition point. In the absence of a magnetic field these will be the changes associated with a second-order transition, such as change in the coefficient of expansion and in the elastic constants but not in the volume. These changes of properties are, however, generally so small that they have only recently been observed by specially sensitive methods.

The transition temperature is a function of the pressure (and stress generally). Thus the Bardeen, Cooper, Schrieffer theory gives the transition point in the form:

$$T_c = 1 \cdot 14 \hbar \omega \exp\left[-1/N(0)A\right]$$

where $N(0)$ is the density of electron states at the Fermi surface in the normal metal, $A$ is a parameter which measures the average interaction between the electrons which arises from a coupling with the lattice vibrations, $\hbar \omega$ is the average phonon energy and is proportional to $\theta_D$. If the only effect of pressure were that on $\theta_D$ the change of $T_c$ with increase of pressure would be positive but the opposite sign has been observed except for thallium at low pressures (Sn: $T_c = 3 \cdot 732 - 4 \cdot 95 \times 10^{-5} P + 3 \cdot 9 \times 10^{-10} P^2$; $P$ in the atmospheres; Swenson). Thus the major contribution to the effect seems to arise from the changes of $N(0)$ and $A$ due to change in volume of the specimen.

The reflectivity of metals for visible light is the same for the super-conducting and normal states but at radio frequencies, as we have seen, the absorptivity of a superconductor approaches very small values as the temperature approaches 0° K. This suggests that the absorptivity at 0° K. changes from very small to approximately that in the normal state in the difficultly accessible region around $\lambda = 0 \cdot 1$ mm. between the far infra-red and microwave wave lengths. A rapid onset of absorption in this region would suggest a quantum effect such as an excitation of the electrons across an energy gap. The onset

8

of absorption has been observed recently mainly as a result of the work of Tinkham and Glover and is in agreement with the existence of an energy spectrum in which there is a gap of about $3 \cdot 5kT_c$ at $0°$ K. decreasing to zero at $T_c$ as is also indicated by the specific heat observations.

The attenuation of ultrasonic waves by a metal is lower in the superconducting state than in the normal state and this effect also suggests an energy spectrum of the type mentioned above.

The thermoelectric e.m.f. between two metals becomes zero when both the metals are superconducting. Furthermore the Thomson effect is zero in a superconductor. This must be interpreted as meaning that the superconducting electrons have zero entropy and so do not convey heat through the metal.

All the phenomena indicate that superconductivity is a process taking place in the conduction electron system though there is a relatively weak but essential coupling with the lattice vibration.

### Penetration Depth and High-Frequency Resistance

The description $B = 0$ is adequate for superconductors of macro-scopic size, but it is obvious that the currents in a superconductor cannot be strictly superficial but must occupy a layer of finite depth below the surface. Correspondingly a magnetic field must penetrate to a certain depth $\lambda$ and the observed susceptibility will be somewhat smaller than corresponds to perfect diamagnetism. If the field decreases exponentially from the surface the field $H$ at a distance $x$ below the surface will be given by $H = H_0 e^{-x/\lambda}$, where $H_0 =$ magnetic field at the surface. For sufficiently small objects the reduction in susceptibility will be observable. Such measurements have been made on an assembly of spheres (mercury colloid) by Shoenberg, of thin wires (Desirant and Shoenberg) and of thin films (Lock) and have indicated the existence of a penetration depth $\lambda$, and a variation of $\lambda$ with temperature given by $(\lambda/\lambda_0)^2 = 1/(1 - (T/T_c)^4)$ where $\lambda_0$, the value at $0°$ K., is of the order of $4$–$6 \times 10^{-6}$ cm. for the various superconducting metals. Since a static magnetic field penetrates completely into a normal conductor, $\lambda$ becomes theoretically infinite at $T_c$. A consequence of the penetration depth is that the observed critical magnetic field should be greater for a superconductor of sufficiently small dimensions than for a large specimen. Resistance measurements have shown this effect to exist (for thin wires – Pontius, for thin films – Shalnikov, Appleyard).

The London theory of superconductivity (see p. 117) predicts that the penetration depth is given by the formula $\lambda = (mc^2/4\pi n_s e^2)^{1/2}$ where $m$ is the effective mass and $n_s$ the effective number of electrons associated with the superconductivity. The similarity in the properties of superfluid helium and superconductors has led to the formulation of a 'two fluid' model for superconductivity. Thus a fraction $x$ of the conduction electrons are regarded as being in an 'uncondensed' or normal state and a fraction $(1-x)$ in a 'condensed' or superconducting state. To fit the observed properties the free energy is written as follows:

$$f_s = -\tfrac{1}{2}x^{1/2}\gamma T^2 - \tfrac{1}{4}(1-x)\gamma T_c^2$$

where $\gamma$ has the same significance as on p. 111. Since the value of $x$ for equilibrium at any temperature is given by $(\partial f_s/\partial x)_T = 0$ and also $x = 1$ for $T = T_c$ we obtain $x = (T/T_c)^4$ and the specific heat per unit volume $c_s = 3\gamma T^3/T_c^2$, thus varying as $T^3$. At the time this relation was supposed to represent the experimental results for the specific heat of metals in the superconducting state but is now known to be only an approximation to the actual exponential temperature variation. When the above expression for $x$ is combined with the London formula for the penetration depth, the formula for $\lambda$ given above is reproduced with $\lambda_0 = (mc^2/4\pi n e^2)^{1/2}$, where $n$ is now the total effective number of electrons per unit volume.

The presence of normal electrons below the transition point $T_c$ is not detectable by direct current measurements, but in the presence of an electric field of sufficiently high frequency it should be possible to show that the total current is the sum of that carried by the normal electrons and by the superconducting electrons. H. London was able to show that the presence of the normal electrons resulted in a generation of heat in the surface layer at a frequency of 1500 megacycles/sec. and hence that a high-frequency resistance occurs in superconductors below the transition point. This high-frequency resistance has since been measured from observations of the $Q$ value of a shorted transmission line made of mercury and of tin at 1200 and 9400 megacycles/sec. (Pippard), and of various superconducting cavity resonators at frequencies up to 23,000 megacycles/sec.

(Maxwell, Marcus and Slater and others). Instead of falling rapidly to zero as the transition point is passed as in the d.c. case, the high-frequency resistance decreases below $T_c$ in the way shown in Table 12, where $R/R_n$ is the ratio of the resistance at temperature $T$ to that present immediately before the transition to the superconducting state. These measurements also showed that the low-temperature resistance in the normal state at these frequencies is much larger

TABLE 12

H.F. Resistance of Tin at
1200 megacycles per sec.
(Pippard)

| $T° K.$ | $100R/R_n$ |
|---|---|
| 3·712 | 100 |
| 3·702 | 70 |
| 3·683₅ | 40 |
| 3·598 | 10 |
| 3·455 | 4 |
| 3·150 | 2 |

than that expected from the observed resistance at higher temperatures. This is due to the fact that at the very low temperatures the mean free path of the electrons is large compared with the depth to which the H.F. current penetrates below the surface (skin effect). This abnormally high resistance in the normal state must be taken in account in evaluating the contribution of the normal electrons to the conductivity in the superconducting state.

**The Nature of Superconductivity**

The quantum mechanical theory of electrical conductivity as developed by Bloch and others has not been able to account for superconductivity. Before it could do so, some form of interaction between the electrons or between them and the lattice would have to be introduced. Ignorance of the correct type of interaction and the mathematical difficulties involved have delayed the successful solution of the problem.

The understanding of superconductivity was advanced when a phenomenological theory was developed by F. and H. London. They succeeded in obtaining a set of equations which reproduce the macroscopic phenomena of superconductivity in much the same way that Maxwell's equations describe the electromagnetic field without enquiring closely into its ultimate origin. The first step in describing the London theory may be taken from an earlier attempt by Becker, Heller and Sauter.

On the basis of Maxwell's equations only, any currents induced in a solid body with an infinite conductivity would be purely surface currents. In any actual case the currents would flow in a layer of small but finite thickness at the surface. In order to determine the distribution of the current in this layer, some additional factor must be taken into account. In the theory of Becker, Heller and Sauter this factor is the inertia of the electrons. By equating the acceleration of the electrons to the force acting on them, we obtain $\dot{J} = E/\Lambda$, where $J$ is the current density, $E$ the electric field existing in the transition layer, $\Lambda = m/ne^2$, $m =$ mass of electron and $n =$ number of electrons per unit volume in the superconducting state. Combining this expression with Maxwell's equation $c\,\mathrm{curl}\,E = -\dot{H}$, we have $\Lambda c\,\mathrm{curl}\,\dot{J} = -\dot{H}$. If $H$ is zero when the body becomes superconducting and a magnetic field is applied subsequently (case I), the above equation yields

$$\Lambda c\,\mathrm{curl}\,J = -H \tag{7}$$

On the other hand, if the body becomes superconducting in a magnetic field $H_0$ and the field is later changed to $H$ (case II), then we obtain

$$\Lambda c\,\mathrm{curl}\,(J-J_0) = -(H-H_0) \tag{8}$$

Equation (7) and its consequences, yet to be discussed correctly, accounts for the observed facts in case I but equation (8) predicts that the induction present in the body at the instant when the latter becomes superconducting will remain frozen-in. The Meissner effect shows that this does not occur for a singly connected body such as a solid sphere or cylinder. The induction is zero in both I and II and equation (7) correctly represents them.

The Londons therefore postulated that equation (7) is the fundamental equation connecting a supercurrent with the magnetic field present, independently of the path by which the superconductivity is produced. Taking the curl of equation (7) and using the Maxwell equation $c\,\mathrm{curl}\,H = 4\pi J$ we obtain

$$\Lambda c^2 \nabla^2 H = 4\pi H \qquad (9)$$

$$\Lambda c^2 \nabla^2 J = 4\pi J \qquad (10)$$

The solution of equation (9) shows that a magnetic field (less than the critical field) penetrates only into a thin superficial layer of a superconductor, decreasing exponentially from the surface inwards. The field falls to $1/e$ of its value at the surface in the distance $\lambda = c\sqrt{(\Lambda/4\pi)}$, so accounting for the Meissner effect for macroscopic superconductors. Equation (10) shows that the supercurrents are similarly restricted to a surface layer of the same thickness.

By combining equation (7), the first of the London equations, with the Maxwell equation $c\,\mathrm{curl}\,E = -\dot{H}$ we obtain

$$\mathrm{curl}\,(E - 4\pi\lambda^2 \dot{J}) = 0$$

which implies that

$$E - \frac{4\pi\lambda^2}{c^2}\dot{J} = \mathrm{grad}\,\phi$$

where $\phi$ is a scalar quantity. In order, however, to agree with the experimentally established facts that a superconductor has a *d.c.* resistance equal to zero and that a static electric field derivable from a potential does *not* penetrate into the surface layer, we must take $\mathrm{grad}\,\phi = 0$ and the second of the London equations becomes

$$E = \frac{4\pi\lambda^2}{c^2}\dot{J} \qquad (11)$$

Equation (11) states that the supercurrent is evoked and maintained by the magnetic field. It indicates that an electric field derived from equation (11) will only be present when there is also a magnetic field which varies with the time. This serves to emphasize the difference between the supercurrent and the normal current on the London theory. The supercurrent is produced and maintained by the (constant) magnetic field present even in the case when the superconductor forms part of a circuit containing a battery and normal conductors. One instance of a current which is governed by a constant magnetic field in the way required by the London theory is already well known, the current produced when a diamagnetic atom is magnetized. In fact, as F. London has pointed out, a superconductor behaves as a single large diamagnetic atom, and it is possible to reverse the procedure and deduce equation (7) from the postulate that the behaviour of the supercurrents in a magnetic field is the same as that of the current in a diamagnetic atom. An equivalent statement is that the wave functions of a superconductor are not appreciably perturbed by the presence of a magnetic field smaller than the critical field in distinction to a normal metal where a magnetic field considerably perturbs the wave functions. Any fundamental theory of superconductivity must reproduce this feature of the London theory. The London theory, as described here, gives an account of superconductivity which is a good first approximation to the observed facts but does not reproduce the finer details such as the anisotropy of the penetration depth in metal crystals. Although the anisotropies leading to a non-tensorial behaviour of the physical properties of a superconductor are now known to be smaller than they were previously supposed to be there is still need for the phenomenological theory to be rewritten in terms of integral equations as a non-local theory involving a further parameter, the coherence length, $\hbar v_0 / k T_c$, where $v_0$ is the Fermi velocity (Pippard).

Many attempts have been made to produce a fundamental theory of superconductivity. They all attempt to find a mechanism whereby, at the transition point, some of the conduction electrons begin to condense into a state of greater order, with an energy gap between this ground state and the excited states of the electrons.

Heisenberg introduced the Coulomb interaction between electrons into the free electron gas model of conductivity and concluded that at low temperatures a portion of the conduction electrons condenses in momentum space into a lattice of wave packets so that a state of higher order is obtained. The calculated lowering of energy is of the order encountered in superconductivity and the condensed electrons are identified with the superconducting electrons of the two fluid model. The calculations involve, however, many approximations and the most definite prediction of the theory is in conflict with experiment.

The isotope effect, that $T_c$ is proportional to $M^{-1/2}$ provides a valuable clue in the search for the mechanism of superconductivity. It shows that there is an interaction between the electrons and the lattice waves and that since superconductivity exists down to absolute zero and disappears at some higher temperature this interaction does not depend on the thermal excitation of the lattice waves.

Fröhlich and also Bardeen have described a subtle form of interaction between electrons and phonons to which they attribute the superconductive properties. An electron causes a local disturbance of the lattice producing a phonon field with which it interacts. This results in a 'self-energy' analogous to that of an electron in the electromagnetic field of which it is itself the source. The 'interaction with itself' due to the phonon field also leads to an apparent interaction with other electrons. This latter effect arises from processes in which an electron emits a phonon which is absorbed by another electron. This electron interaction produces an electron ground state lower than that in the absence of such an interaction. The difference in energy is of the same order of magnitude as the difference in energy between the superconducting and normal states. Owing to the great mathematical difficulty of the problem, particularly that of separating the small interaction energy from the much larger self-energy, it has not been possible for Fröhlich or Bardeen to show that this interaction leads unequivocally to the properties of a superconductor, zero resistance and the Meissner effect. However, this electron interaction through the medium of the electron–phonon interaction led to the prediction of the isotope effect before it was discovered experimentally.

It appeared that the theories of Fröhlich and Bardeen contained an essential feature of any final theory but needed restating in a more tractable fashion.

The next step towards a theory of superconductivity was made by Cooper who showed that when the electron interaction is attractive the electrons will form pairs and the ground state will then be lower than that for free electrons. The two electrons in the pair have opposite momenta and spins so the pairs behave as quasi-particles of zero spin. This removes one of the difficulties in any theory of superconductivity, how an assembly of electrons, which, as free particles, obey Fermi statistics, can show properties similar to those of the atoms of $He^4$ which obey Bose-Einstein statistics. The electron pairs are, however, not highly localized: but spread over a distance of about $10^{-4}$ cm., the order of magnitude of the coherence length (Pippard).

By a suitable choice of wave functions which resulted in all electrons being correlated in pairs with equal and opposite momenta, Bardeen, Cooper and Schrieffer (1957) succeeded in deducing the characteristics of the ground state of the metal and the excited states. These described a system of electrons in which a condensation had occurred and in which the ground state was separated from the first excited states, by an energy gap, the width of which decreased from a value $3.5\,kT_c$ at $0°$ K. to zero at a higher temperature, $T_c$. Thus the authors were able to derive all the thermodynamic properties of the system and found a good quantitative agreement with the known thermodynamic properties of superconductors. The critical field at any temperature could also be determined by equating $H_c^2/8\pi$ to the condensation energy per unit volume.

The possibility of a resistanceless current flow was also made plausible though no completely satisfactory account can yet be given of the Meissner effect.

Bardeen, Cooper and Schrieffer had to introduce many assumptions and simplifications in their calculations. Bogolyubov has, however, more recently reproduced their results by other and more rigorous mathematical methods.

It is of interest that the 'size' of the electron pair appears as an important parameter in the theory. If this parameter is small compared with the penetration depth of a field into a superconductor there is a local relation between current and field potential and the London equations are obtained. If the parameter on the other hand, is large compared with the penetration depth there is no such local relation between the current and field potential and the Pippard non-local equations are obtained.

Summarizing it may be said that the nature of the interaction which produces superconductivity is now understood and many of its consequences can be accurately calculated. Many details have, however, still to be investigated theoretically.

## CHAPTER VI

# Magnetism

## Ferromagnetism

Weiss has shown that the main phenomena of ferromagnetism can be explained by the assumption that ferromagnetic substances are built up of small domains which are spontaneously magnetized under the influence of a strong intermolecular magnetic field. The nature of this intermolecular field was obscure until Heisenberg showed that it originates in the quantum mechanical exchange integral. The latter has no classical counterpart, and is associated with the difference in Coulomb interaction energy of electrons when the spins are parallel or antiparallel. When the substance is unmagnetized the directions of magnetization of the individual domains are distributed at random. The effect of an external magnetic field is to increase the size of favourably oriented domains at the expense of unfavourably oriented domains and to rotate the direction of magnetization of the domains without appreciably increasing its value. At low temperatures saturation as ordinarily measured therefore represents the magnitude of the spontaneous magnetization of the domains at the temperature of the experiment. As the temperature is lowered the measured saturation becomes more and more nearly equal to the absolute saturation when the carriers of the magnetic moment have all the same direction in all the domains.

The most important problems in ferromagnetism at low temperatures are therefore the determination of the law of approach to saturation as a function of the temperature and the estimation of the intensity of the spontaneous magnetization at absolute zero.

The earlier work on the subject is that of Weiss and Forrer on iron, nickel, magnetite and cementite, and of Allen and Constant on the

---

† It is assumed in this chapter that the reader is familiar with the contents of *Magnetism*, by E. C. Stoner (Methuen's Monographs on Physical Subjects). For a more detailed account see *The Theory of Electric and Magnetic Susceptibilities*, by J. H. van Vleck (Oxford University Press), or *Modern Magnetism*, by L. F. Bates (Cambridge University Press).

cubic modification of cobalt, all for temperatures down to about 90° K. The later work of Fallot on iron, nickel and various iron alloys extended the temperature range to 20° K. Although an accurate knowledge of the temperature variation of the spontaneous magnetization at low temperatures is of considerable importance from the theoretical point of view, it presents a difficult experimental problem on account of the small variation observed at these temperatures. Thus with most ferromagnetic substances the spontaneous magnetization at 100° K. is within 2 parts in 100 of the absolute saturation and in some cases within 2–3 parts in 1000.

The magnetization at any temperature was found for high field strengths to be given by

$$\sigma_{H,T} = \sigma_{\infty,T}(1 - a/H) \tag{1}$$

in which $\sigma_{H,T}$ is the observed magnetization for a field strength $H$ and temperature $T$, $\sigma_{\infty,T}$ is the apparent saturation at temperature $T$, $H$ is the applied magnetic field corrected for the demagnetizing effect of the specimen and $a$ is the coefficient of magnetic hardness which varies with the temperature and the nature of the sample. The observations down to 90° K. of the temperature variation of the apparent saturation can be represented by the expression

$$\sigma_{\infty,T} = \sigma_{\infty,0}(1 - AT^2 - BT^4) \tag{2}$$

in which $\sigma_{\infty,0}$ is the absolute saturation, and $A$ and $B$ are constants. For iron and cementite $B$ in equation (2) is zero and for the other ferromagnetics mentioned it is small compared with $A$.

Somewhat later Bloch deduced an expression for the temperature approach to saturation at low temperatures, using the Heisenberg theory of the molecular field. For the temperature variation of $\sigma_{\infty,T}$ Bloch found

$$\sigma_{\infty,T} = \sigma_{\infty,0}(1 - cT^{3/2}) \tag{3}$$

in which $c$ is a constant dependent on the crystal structure of the ferromagnetic. Expressions (2) and (3) are indistinguishable when applied to the observations above 90° K. On the other hand, Fallot's data below 90° K. agree very well with (3) and show deviations much larger than the errors of observation when compared with (2). For the ratio of the absolute saturation to the apparent saturation at room temperature, $\sigma_{\infty,0}/\sigma_{\infty,288}$ Fallot found the values 1·0190 for iron and 1·0570 for nickel. The absolute saturation magnetizations deduced from these observations are 12390·4 erg/oe. gram atom for iron, 3373·8 for nickel and 9500 for cobalt. These correspond to 2·2, 0·61 and 1·7 Bohr magnetons per atom respectively.

More recent work on ferromagnetism at low temperatures has been concerned with the investigation of the properties of ferro-magnetics observed to have Curie points below room temperature, such as the rare-earth metals, gadolinium (Curie point 289° K.), terbium (230° K.), dysprosium (105° K.) and holmium (20° K.) and various compounds, for example uranium hydride $UH_3$ (180° K.). In addition theoretical studies have been made by Néel and experimental studies by Weil on ferromagnetic materials in the form of small particles either as powders or enclosed in a non-ferromagnetic matrix. It is established that for any temperature there is a minimum volume of the particle below which the material is not ferromagnetic.

Ferromagnetic substances exhibit their typical properties of hysteresis and remanence below the Curie point at which the dis-appearance of the ferromagnetism is accompanied by a marked anomaly in the specific heat generally similar to that at the $\lambda$-point of liquid $He^4$. Specific heat anomalies, hysteresis and remanence are also observed with the salts used for adiabatic demagnetization at temperatures in the range 0·1–0·001° K. The phenomena are, how-ever, different in many ways from those shown by ferromagnetics at higher temperatures and are now classed under the headings of anti-ferromagnetism. Some account of them is given in a later section.

The possibility of a nuclear ferromagnetism in metals has already been mentioned.

### Diamagnetism
The non-conducting elements and compounds, the molecules of which possess no permanent magnetic moment, are diamagnetic and their molecular susceptibilities (specific susceptibility × molecular weight) are, in general, independent of the temperature and the strength of the applied magnetic field. This is, however, not the case with the metals and semiconductors, the (negative) susceptibility generally increasing as the temperature is lowered and in most cases

showing remarkable variations with applied magnetic field at very low temperatures. (de Haas-van Alphen effect, see next section.)

The susceptibilities of polycrystalline specimens of most of the diamagnetic elements have been determined by Honda and by Owen down to the temperature of liquid air. Their work was later extended to $14.2°$ K. by de Haas and van Alphen. In addition, the magnetic properties of single crystals of some of the diamagnetic metals have been determined by McLennan, Ruedy and Cohen. The case of

TABLE 13

| $T°K.$ | $\chi \times 10^6$ | | | | | | | |
|---|---|---|---|---|---|---|---|---|
| | | | | | | | Bi | |
| | *Graphite* | Cu | Ag | Cd | Pb | Tl | $\perp$ *Hexag. axis* | $\parallel$ *Hexag. axis* |
| 289 | −3·0 | −0·086 | −0·188 | −0·183 | −0·111 | −0·215 | −1·48 | −1·045 |
| 77·2 | 4·7 | 0·090 | 0·191 | 0·245 | 0·129 | 0·246 | 1·80 | — |
| 63·8 | 4·7 | 0·091 | 0·190 | 0·256 | 0·131 | 0·248 | −1·80 | — |
| 20·4 | 4·7 | 0·097 | 0·190 | 0·319 | 0·132 | 0·255 | depends on field | 1·20 |
| 14·2 | −4·7 | 0·097 | 0·190 | 0·326 | 0·132 | 0·258 | | −1·20 |

bismuth is of particular interest. It has been shown by Goetz and Focke that the very large negative susceptibility of bismuth is changed to a remarkable extent by the presence of very small quantities of other elements.

Table 13 gives some typical results for the diamagnetic metals and graphite as measured by de Haas and van Alphen. It will be seen that the negative susceptibility increases with decrease in temperature, the rate of increase becoming smaller as the temperature falls.

The susceptibility of the diamagnetic metals and semiconductors is the sum of three contributions, (1) the diamagnetism of the ions, (2) the Pauli paramagnetism of the conduction electrons and (3) the

Landau diamagnetism of the latter. The contribution due to the diamagnetism of the ions is

$$\chi_A(\mathrm{I}) = -\frac{Ze^2 \Sigma \overline{r^2}}{6mc^2}$$

in which $Z$ is the number of atoms per gram-atom, $e$ the electronic charge, $m$ the mass of the electron and $\Sigma\overline{r^2}$ the mean of the square of the radius of the electron orbit summed over all possible values. $\chi_A(\mathrm{I})$ is thus independent of the temperature and field strength.

Pauli was the first to show that a gas of free electrons, each having a spin moment $\mu$ and conforming to the Fermi statistics, shows a weak paramagnetism which is independent of the temperature. A more general calculation by Bloch shows that this contribution to the atomic susceptibility amounts to

$$\chi_A(\mathrm{II}) = +\left[\frac{12m\mu^2}{h^2}\left(\frac{n}{V}\right)^{1/3}\left(\frac{\pi}{3}\right)^{2/3} - \frac{64\pi^4 Vm^3\mu^2 k^2 T^2}{9nh^6}\right]$$

$$= 2 \cdot 20 \times 10^{-14}\left(\frac{n}{V}\right)^{1/3} - 1 \cdot 03 \times 10^7 T^2\left(\frac{V}{n}\right) \qquad (4)$$

$n$ = number of conduction electrons in the volume $V$. Since $n/V$ is of the order $10^{22}$, the second term is quite negligible at low temperatures and the atomic susceptibility is approximately equal to $10^{-6}$ and independent of the temperature. This result is not materially changed when the conduction electrons are not considered as 'free', but as bound loosely to the metallic ions as in Bloch's theory of electrical conduction in metals.

The corresponding calculation for the case of semiconductors (Wilson) gives a different result as the number of electrons in the various bands of allowed energies varies appreciably with the temperature. The formula is

$$\chi_A(\mathrm{II}) = +\frac{\mu^2\pi^{2/3}}{V\beta}\left(\frac{T}{T_0}\right)^{1/2} e^{-\theta/T} \quad \text{for } T \ll \theta \qquad (5)$$

in which $\beta = kT_0$, $k\theta = W_0 - W_1$ and $\beta$, $W_0$ and $W_1$ are quantities of the nature of energies connected with the first and second allowed band of energies of the conduction electrons. The paramagnetic susceptibility, in this case, decreases exponentially with fall in temperature in agreement with the behaviour of graphite.

When effects due to 'spin' are neglected a 'gas' of free electrons contributes nothing to the susceptibility on the classical theory. Landau has however, shown that the quantum theory leads to a weak diamagnetism for such an electron gas, the effect being a consequence of the fact that the angular momentum of the (bent) electron paths in a magnetic field must satisfy certain quantum conditions. The susceptibility so calculated for free electrons is of the opposite sign to (4) and equal to one-third of the first term. It is therefore also independent of the temperature.

## De Haas-Van Alphen Effect

The magnetic properties of single crystals of pure bismuth at low temperatures were studied first by de Haas and van Alphen and later by Shoenberg. The susceptibilities exhibit remarkable periodic variations with field strength. Fig. 28 shows the magnetization perpendicular to the hexagonal axis of the crystal as a function of the magnetic field at $20.4°$ K. and $14.2°$ K. The susceptibility calculated from these observations is thus a periodic function of the field, the variations being more marked at the lower temperature. On the other hand, the susceptibility parallel to the hexagonal axis is independent of the field down to $14.2°$ K.

As a result of the work of Sydoriak and Robinson and of Lazarev and, to a predominating extent, of Shoenberg the de Haas-van Alphen effect has been observed with Bi, Zn, Ga, C (graphite), Sb, Al, Hg, Tl, Sn, In, Cd, Be, Mg, Pb, Mo, As and W. Up till recently the effect had not been observed in any monovalent metal but in 1959 Shoenberg discovered the effect in a very pure, very perfect small crystal of copper (copper whisker) and later also in silver and gold. The work has shown that the period of the oscillations is accurately proportional to $1/H$ and that more than one period may be present.

The explanation of the de Haas-van Alphen effect began when Peierls extended Landau's calculation of electronic diamagnetism to the case of low temperatures and high field strengths for more or less tightly bound electrons. He showed that the susceptibility is then a function of the applied field. The magnetization shows a series of minima which become more pronounced and more numerous the lower the temperature and the positions of which satisfy the relation $H = \text{const.}/m$, $m = 1, 2, 3$, etc. This is qualitatively what was observed by de Haas and van Alphen for bismuth but there is not a quantitative agreement between experiment and the theory in its simplest form. The calculations, however, indicate that the effect should be observed most readily with metals having a large diamagnetism and a small number of 'free' electrons per atom, as in bismuth, antimony and gallium.

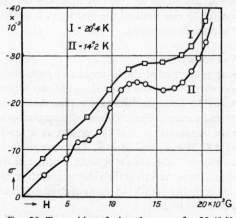

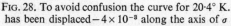

FIG. 28. To avoid confusion the curve for 20·4° K. has been displaced $-4 \times 10^{-3}$ along the axis of $\sigma$

Peierls' theory was worked out for the case of an isotropic metal. It was later extended by Blackman and by Landau to take into account the actual crystalline nature of the metal and a much better agreement with more detailed experimental work was obtained. The results show that the motions of the electrons contributing to the de Haas-van Alphen effect are very anisotropic and that only a small number of the 'conduction electrons' (about $10^{-3}$ to $10^{-6}$ per atom) with a small effective mass ($0.1\ m_e$) are responsible for the observations at moderate magnetic field strengths. Dingle later showed that the remaining discrepancies between theory and experiment are removed if the energy levels of the electrons are broadened by collision or some other process.

The whole aspect of the subject changed, however, when Onsager showed in 1952 that the period of the de Haas-van Alphen oscillations is inversely proportional to the extreme cross-sectional area of the Fermi surface of the metal by planes normal to the magnetic field. An extension of the work by Lifshitz and Kosevich and by Lifshitz and Pogorelov has shown that the observations of the oscillations can be used to specify the Fermi surface completely. The low to moderate field strengths give information of the shape of those outer parts of the Fermi surface which are close to the boundary of the Brillouin zone and which contain only a few electrons. To obtain a more extensive knowledge of the surface much larger field strengths must be used as in the recent work of Shoenberg (up to 100,000 oe.). Thus the de Haas-van Alphen effect has become a valuable method for the investigation of the constant energy surfaces of the electrons in metals.

In this way it has been shown that the observed effect in bismuth corresponds to the presence of three ellipsoidal surfaces making angles of 120° with each other. On the other hand, in copper the Fermi surface consists of an approximate sphere with eight necks directed towards the hexagonal surfaces of the first Brillouin zone.

## Paramagnetism

When the atoms or molecules of a substance have a quantum number which is not zero, they possess a permanent magnetic moment and the substance exhibits paramagnetism. The susceptibility is positive, generally independent of the magnetic field strength and approximately inversely proportional to the absolute temperature.

By considering the free energy of the system and applying a well-known theorem in statistical mechanics, it can be shown that the susceptibility $\chi$ per unit mass is given by

$$\chi = -\frac{N}{H} \cdot \frac{\sum\limits_{s} (\partial E_s / \partial H) e^{-E_s/kT}}{\sum\limits_{s} e^{-E_s/kT}} \qquad (6)$$

In the above expression $N$ is the number of atoms or molecules per gm., $E_s$ the energy of the $s$th state of the atom or molecule, and the summation extends over all states which make an appreciable contribution to the susceptibility. The problem of calculating $\chi$ thus

9

reduces to that of calculating the possible energy levels in the presence of a magnetic field.

On account of the Boltzmann factor $e^{-E_s/kT}$ the magnitude of the susceptibility and its variation with temperature depend greatly on the energy separation between states, a state making an appreciable contribution or not at the temperature $T$, according as the height of the state above the lowest one is small or large compared with $kT$. In general the possible states are the components of the lowest multiplet. Thus in the case of the trivalent cerium ion, the lowest multiplet is a $^2F$, the two components $^2F_{5/2}$ and $^2F_{7/2}$ being separated by an energy difference of 2513 cm.$^{-1}$.† Since this is large compared with $kT$,‡ only the ground state $^2F_{5/2}$ will contribute appreciably to the susceptibility at low temperatures.

Since, owing to the intervention of other states beside the ground state, the variation of the susceptibility with temperature is not in general a strict inverse proportionality to the absolute temperature, it is convenient to characterize the atom or molecule by its 'effective magneton number' defined by

$$\mu_{\text{eff}}^2 = \frac{3\chi kT}{N\beta^2} = \frac{3\chi_{\text{mol}}RT}{(5564)^2}$$

in which $\mu_{\text{eff}}$ is the effective Bohr magneton number, $N$ the number of atoms or molecules per unit mass, $\chi$ the susceptibility per unit mass and $\chi_{\text{mol}}$ the molecular susceptibility. $\mu_{\text{eff}}$ will in general vary with the temperature and will only be equal to the permanent magnetic moment of the atom or molecule when the substance obeys Curie's law, $\chi T =$ const.

### Gases

There exist only two paramagnetic gases which can be investigated at low temperatures, oxygen and nitric oxide. They are of particular interest on account of the great contrast between the temperature variation of the susceptibility in the two cases.

Expression (6), when applied to the case of a diatomic molecule, leads to simple formulae for the susceptibility in the two limiting cases of the multiplet intervals being small or very large compared

† For the free ion.     ‡ $kT$ at room temperature = about 200 cm.$^{-1}$.

with $kT$. In the first case the population of the sub-levels of the ground state is independent of the temperature and the formula becomes

$$\chi = \frac{N\beta^2}{3kT}[4S(S+1)+\Lambda^2] \tag{7}$$

in which $S$ is the quantum number connected with the total spin moment of the molecule and $\Lambda$ that of the component of the orbital angular momentum along the line joining the two nuclei. For a $^3\Sigma$ state, as in oxygen (separation $h\Lambda\nu$ of the three sub-levels about 1 cm.$^{-1}$), $S=1$ and $\Lambda=0$, so that the molecular susceptibility of this gas should be given by $\chi_{mol}= 8L\beta^2/3kT= 0\cdot993/T$ ($L=$ number of molecules in the gm. mol.). $\chi_{mol}$ should therefore be equal to $3\cdot39 \times 10^{-3}$ at 20° C. and the gas should obey Curie's law.

The susceptibility of oxygen at low temperatures has been measured by Woltjer, Coopoolse and Wiersma (down to 157° K.), by Stössel (down to 136·5° K.) and by Wiersma, de Haas and Capel (down to 77·6° K.). While Stössel finds the Curie law to be obeyed accurately, the Leiden workers claim that this is only approximately the case, small deviations occurring which, according to Wiersma and Gorter, are due to the presence of a small number of $O_4$ molecules in the gas. The observed molecular susceptibility at 20° C. is $3\cdot42 \times 10^{-3}$ (Woltjer, Coopoolse and Wiersma), other values at room temperature being $3\cdot48 \times 10^{-3}$ (Wills and Hector) and $3\cdot34 \times 10^{-3}$ (Lehrer).

When the multiplet separations of the ground state are large compared with $kT$, only the lowest sub-level is occupied and the formula for a diatomic molecule becomes

$$\chi = \frac{N\beta^2}{3kT}(\Lambda+2\Sigma)^2 \tag{8}$$

in which $\Sigma$ gives the component of the spin moment along the line joining the two nuclei of the molecule. No paramagnetic diatomic molecule satisfying this formula at room temperature is known. The ground state of nitric oxide is a normal $^2\pi$ state ($^2\pi_{1/2}$ has a lower energy than $^2\pi_{3/2}$, separation $\Delta\nu= 120\cdot9$ cm.$^{-1}$, $S= \frac{1}{2}$, $\Lambda= 1$) with a multiplet interval comparable with $kT$. Its magneton number should therefore be 0 at absolute zero as given by (8) and 2 at a very high temperature, as given by (7), with intermediate values at intermediate temperatures. The population of the two sub-levels will vary appreciably with the temperature and expression (6) must be used without the simplification introduced in deducing (7) and (8). Van Vleck has shown that for this general case the susceptibility is given by

$$\chi = \frac{\theta^2 \beta^2}{3kT} \tag{9}$$

with

$$\theta = 4\left(\frac{1 - e^{-x} + x e^{-x}}{x + x e^{-x}}\right)$$

and

$$x = h\Delta v / kT$$

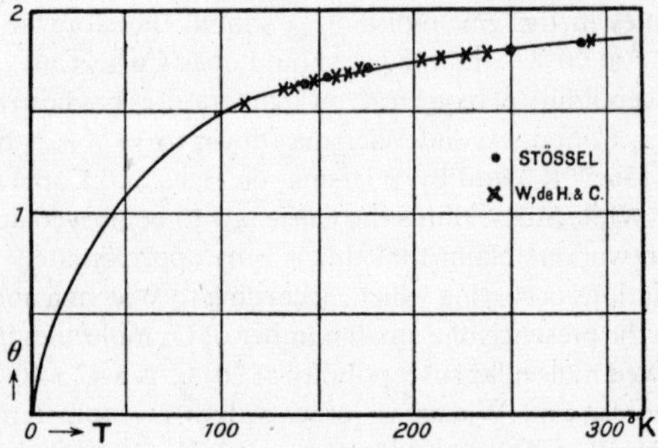

FIG. 29

$\theta$ is therefore the effective magneton number and varies with the temperature as indicated by the curve in Fig. 29.

The theory has been tested experimentally by Bitter, by Aharoni and Scherrer, by Stössel, and by Wiersma, de Haas and Capel. The two last mentioned series of observations are the most extensive, and have been plotted in Fig. 29. It will be seen that the agreement with the theoretical curve is excellent. The effective magneton number varies from 1·852 at 292·1° K. to 1·535 at 112·8° K.; a striking contrast to the behaviour of oxygen.

## Solids

The great majority of the determinations of the susceptibilities of paramagnetic solids have been made on the powdered substance. The measurements at low temperatures have been made (1) by measuring the force exerted on the sample in a magnetic field or (2) by determining the mutual inductance of a pair of coils, containing the sample, by means of a very sensitive a.c. bridge. The first method may take two forms. In the one case a glass or quartz tube is filled with the powder to form a long 'rod' one end of which is placed on the axis of the pole-pieces of the electromagnet while the other is situated outside the pole-pieces where the field is almost negligible. A force then acts on the sample given by $F = \frac{1}{2}\chi m(H_1^2 - H_2^2)/l$ (I), where $F$ is the force, $m$ the mass of the substance, $H_1$ and $H_2$ the magnetic fields at the two ends of the sample and $l$ is the length of the latter.

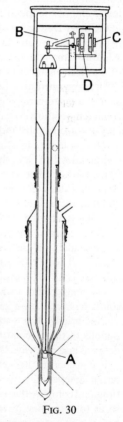

Fig. 30

In the other method a small sample is placed in a non-homogeneous magnetic field when a force acts on it given by $F = \chi m H \, dH/dx$ (II), in which $dH/dx$ is the gradient of the magnetic field in the direction in which the force is measured. At very low temperatures $\chi$ may be a function of $H$ and (II) is replaced by $F = \sigma m \, dH/dx$, where $\sigma$ is the magnetization per unit mass. The apparatus used by different observers differs greatly in the methods of measurement of the force and of maintenance of the low temperatures. One typical example may be described. Fig. 30 shows diagrammatically the apparatus used by Gorter, de Haas and van den Handel for the measurement of the susceptibility of potassium chromium alum down to $1\cdot34°$ K. The specimen A hangs by a quartz rod from one arm of a balance B. The force on A is measured by balancing it against the force produced between a fixed coil C and a movable coil D, attached to the other arm of the balance, when a suitable current is sent through the coils.

The specimen is surrounded by a long metal tube attached to the balance case so that the whole forms an airtight system which can be filled with helium gas to provide the necessary thermal conduction between the cooling bath and the substance under investigation. The lower end of the metal tube is immersed in a bath of liquid helium in the inner Dewar vessel shown, and the latter is protected by liquid hydrogen in the outer Dewar vessel. The lower portions of both vessels are of small diameter so that they can be placed between the poles of the electromagnet as shown.

The experimental results of the investigation of paramagnetic solids at low temperatures may be briefly summarized as follows. From room temperature down to some temperature which varies considerably from one substance to another, the susceptibility is given by $\chi(T+\varDelta)=$ const., in which $\varDelta$ is a constant. In certain cases $\varDelta$ is small compared with $1°$ and then the substance obeys the simple law down to the lowest temperature investigated. In general, however, the susceptibility deviates from this law below some definite temperature and may increase either more or less rapidly with fall in temperature than is given by the linear relation between $1/\chi$ and $T$.

The constant $\varDelta$ is greatly dependent on the nature of the substance, being smaller the greater the magnetic dilution of the molecule. For example $\varDelta$ for $Pr_2(SO_4)_3 . 8H_2O$ is $32°$, while that of the anhydrous sulphate is $45°$. It is positive for purely paramagnetic substances.

The temperature variation of the susceptibilities of paramagnetic solids has received a satisfactory explanation which we shall now outline briefly. The discussion will be largely restricted to the compounds of the rare earth elements, as these have received the most detailed and extensive theoretical treatment.

In considering the theoretical interpretation of the observations on paramagnetic solids, we shall first make the simplest possible assumptions and compare the results so obtained with the experimental values so as to determine in what directions the theory must be extended before a complete explanation can be obtained.

Let us first suppose the paramagnetic ions in the solid are completely free, that is, are subject to no external influence but that of the applied magnetic field and that the energy separations between the components of the fundamental multiplet of the ion are very large compared with $kT$. This is reasonable for the rare earth ions where the magnetic moment is due to an incomplete $4f$ shell of electrons largely shielded from external influences by an outer complete shell of electrons. Only the ground state, $J = L - S$ or $L + S$, according as the multiplet is 'normal' or 'inverted', will then contribute to the susceptibility and, if we neglect a term which is independent of the temperature and is usually small, (6) reduces to

$$\chi = \frac{Ng^2\beta^2 J(J+1)}{3kT} \tag{10}$$

in which $g$ is the Lande factor and is equal to

$$1 + \frac{J(J+1) + S(S+1) - L(L+1)}{2J(J+1)}$$

(10) has been applied by Hund with considerable success to the compounds of the rare earths. By applying certain empirical rules Hund was able to deduce which of the possible states of an ion of a given electronic configuration is the ground state. Column 2 of Table 14 gives the ground state so deduced for the trivalent ions of the rare earths, assuming the multiplets are normal in the first half of the group and inverted in the second half. Column 3 gives the Bohr magneton numbers calculated from the data of column 2 by means of the formula $\mu_{\text{eff}}^2 = g^2 J(J+1)$.

The values in column 3 may be compared with those of $\mu_{\text{eff}}$ (column 5), deduced from observations on solids at room temperature, assuming the validity of Curie's law. It will be seen that with the exception of Sm and Eu there is general agreement. The discrepancies with Sm and Eu are, however, of particular interest as showing one direction in which the simple theory needs extension. As van Vleck and Franck have shown, we must discard the assumption that the multiplet intervals are large compared with $kT$. We may then have contributions to the susceptibility from all the $2J + 1$ components of the fundamental multiplet, and we must also retain the term previously neglected. (6) then becomes

$$\chi = \frac{N \sum\limits_{L-S}^{L+S} \{[g_J^2\beta^2 J(J+1)/3kT] + \alpha_J\}(2J+1)\, e^{-E_J^0/kT}}{\sum e^{-E_J^0/kT}(2J+1)} \tag{11}$$

$E_J^0$ is the energy of the state with quantum number $J$ in the absence of the magnetic field, and $\alpha_J$ is the term independent of the temperature which van Vleck has shown to enter necessarily into the quantum mechanical calculation of $\chi$ and which can be interpreted physically as the contribution of the component of magnetic moment perpendicular to the angular momentum vector.

TABLE 14

| $+ + +$ Ion | Ground state | $\mu_{\text{eff}}$ (Hund) | $\mu_{\text{eff}}$ (v.V. and F.) | $\mu_{\text{eff}}$ (Expt.) |
|---|---|---|---|---|
| La | $^1S$ | 0·00 | 0·00 | Diamagnetic |
| Ce | $^2F_{5/2}$ | 2·54 | 2·56 | 2·43, 2·39, 2·27 |
| Pr | $^3H_4$ | 3·58 | 3·62 | 3·40, 3·60, 3·52 |
| Nd | $^4I_{9/2}$ | 3·62 | 3·68 | 3·60, 3·62, 3·52 |
| Pm | $^5I_4$ | 2·68 | 2·83 | |
| Sm | $^6H_{5/2}$ | 0·84 | 1·55 | 1·56, 1·54, 1·53 |
| Eu | $^7F_0$ | 0·00 | 3·40 | 3·60, 3·64, 3·34 |
| Gd | $^8S$ | 7·94 | 7·94 | 7·87, 8·18, 7·78 |
| Tb | $^7F_6$ | 9·7 | 9·7 | 9·60, 9·62, 9·35 |
| Dy | $^6H_{15/2}$ | 10·6 | 10·6 | 10·50, 10·63, 10·51 |
| Ho | $^5I_8$ | 10·6 | 10·6 | 10·45, 10·63, 10·45 |
| Er | $^4I_{15/2}$ | 9·6 | 9·6 | 9·43, 9·58, 9·34 |
| Tu | $^3H_6$ | 7·6 | 7·6 | 7·52, 7·11 |
| Yb | $^2F_{7/2}$ | 4·5 | 4·5 | 4·34, 4·57, 4·42 |
| Lu | $^1S$ | 0·00 | 0·00 | Diamagnetic |

To evaluate (11) we must know the positions of the energy levels $E_J$. The actual multiplet intervals of the trivalent ions of the rare earths have not been determined spectroscopically but they can be calculated from a formula by Goudsmit giving the overall width of the multiplet, that is the energy separation between the outermost components, $J = L - S$ and $J = L + S$. The actual intervals between the various components can be obtained by applying the rule that while the overall width is proportional to $\frac{1}{2}[J_{max}(J_{max}+1)-J_{min}(J_{min}+1)]$ the interval between the components $J$ and $J+1$ is proportional to $J+1$. The multiplet intervals calculated in this way for $Ce^{+++}$, $Pr^{+++}$, $Nd^{+++}$, $Sm^{+++}$ and $Eu^{+++}$ are given in Fig. 31.

At low temperatures we are mainly concerned with the interval between the lowest and the next higher energy level. For the ions mentioned above this interval is 2513, 2113, 1813, 932 and 255 cm.$^{-1}$

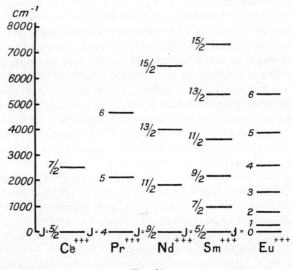

FIG. 31

respectively. Thus, since $kT$ at room temperature is about 200 cm.$^{-1}$, the contribution of the higher level to the susceptibility will be appreciable at this temperature for samarium and europium, but very small for the other ions. Column 4 gives the values of $\mu_{eff}$ (room temperature) calculated by van Vleck and Franck using the more general expression (11). It will be seen that the discrepancies for samarium and europium have now disappeared, while the agreement in the other cases remains as good as before. According to (11) the susceptibilities of samarium and europium compounds will deviate greatly from Curie's law. Their theoretical temperature variations have been calculated by van Vleck and Franck for a wide range of temperatures. We shall not deal with these calculations here, as the measurements do not agree well with the theoretical values, because there is still another factor or group of factors to be considered in the complete treatment of the problem. We have so far considered the ions as 'free' whereas they are undoubtedly acted upon by relatively large and generally asymmetric electrostatic fields due to the presence of the surrounding atoms or ions in the crystal. The effect of this 'crystalline field' is similar to the Stark effect in free atoms, that is, each level of the ion is split up into a number of sub-levels. Bethe has calculated theoretically the effect of such a field on any given ground state of the ion and has shown that the magnitude of the splitting and the number of components depend on the magnitude and symmetry of the crystalline field. The energies of the components in the absence of a magnetic field having been determined by Bethe's theory, their energies in the presence of a magnetic field can be calculated and inserted into (6) to obtain the susceptibility. It has thus been found possible to account quantitatively for the variation of $\mu_{\text{eff}}$ in various cases from room temperature down to about $1°$ K. by suitably choosing the symmetry of the crystalline field and the magnitude of the constants involved. It is not in general possible to calculate the potential of the crystalline field from a knowledge of the crystal structure of the substance. The theory is too complicated to reproduce here in detail, but some of its general features will be outlined and illustrated with the aid of a few definite examples.

The effect of the crystalline field on any state of the free ion may be summarized as follows: (1) A highly asymmetric field splits up the level into its maximum number of components, $2J+1$ when the ion contains an even number of electrons, i.e. $J$ is integral, but when the ion contains an odd number of electrons, i.e. $J$ is half-integral, the components consist of $J+\frac{1}{2}$ pairs of coincident levels (Kramers degeneracy), each component being doubly degenerate. This remaining degeneracy is only lifted by a magnetic field. This fact has a very important bearing on the behaviour of $\mu_{\text{eff}}$ for odd and even ions at lowest temperatures. (2) In a more symmetrical field the number of components is less than the maximum, due to some of the levels being further degenerate. (3) The crystalline field has to a first order of approximation no effect on an $S$ state. Ions whose ground state is an $S$ state therefore behave in a solid to this degree of approximation as if they were free and Curie's law is found to hold over a wide range of temperature. Thus for example, gadolinium sulphate (ground state $^8S$) obeys Curie's law for weak magnetic fields down to $1\cdot3^\circ$ K. (Woltjer and Kamerlingh Onnes), and manganese ammonium sulphate (ground state $^6S$) down to $14^\circ$ K. (Jackson and Kamerlingh Onnes). There is, however, a small second-order effect which is of great importance in the region of temperatures below $1^\circ$ K. The ground state of the $Gd^{+++}$ ion in gadolinium sulphate is now known to be split into four doubly degenerate levels with an overall splitting of $0\cdot82$ cm.$^{-1}$.

Since an $S$ state ion behaves as if it were free it is to be expected that crystals containing such ions will be very nearly magnetically isotropic independently of the crystalline symmetry of the substance. This has proved to be the case. For substances containing paramagnetic ions whose ground state is not an $S$ state, the crystal may be highly anisotropic magnetically, the degree of anisotropy often becoming very large at lowest temperatures. Thus in ferrous fluosilicate (trigonal crystal) the ratio of $\chi_\perp$ to $\chi_\parallel$ ($\chi_\perp$, $\chi_\parallel$ susceptibility respectively perpendicular and parallel to the trigonal axis) rises from $1\cdot7$ at $77^\circ$ K. to $160$ at $1\cdot6^\circ$ K. The temperature variation of the two susceptibilities is very different at low temperatures and yet the average susceptibility follows the law $\chi(T+1) = $ const. down to $14^\circ$ K. This shows that much information is lost by measuring only the average susceptibility on a powdered sample.

As an early example of crystalline field calculations the interpretation of the experimental data on $CeF_3$ may be considered. The observations of de Haas and Gorter have shown that this substance obeys the law $\chi(T+62) = $ const. from room temperature down to about $140^\circ$ K. From this temperature down to $14^\circ$ K. the susceptibility increases more and more rapidly with decrease in temperature than is given by the above expression. Kramers showed that these observations can be quantitatively reproduced by assuming a crystalline field of trigonal symmetry in agreement with the crystallographic symmetry of the crystal. The ground state $^2F_{5/2}$ is then split into three doubly degenerate levels. Agreement with the experimental results is obtained if the levels have the following separations, $E_1 = 0$,

$E_2 = 113$ cm.$^{-1}$, $E_3 = 489$ cm.$^{-1}$. For the higher temperatures the susceptibility is found to be given by

$$\chi = \frac{Ng^2\beta^2 J(J+1)}{3kT} + \frac{K}{T^3}$$

This can be written in the form $\chi(T+\Delta) = $ const. if $\Delta$ is now allowed to vary with the temperature. In this way we obtain the following values for $\Delta$.

| $T$ | 50° | 100° | 150° | 200° | 300° |
|---|---|---|---|---|---|
| $\Delta$ | 51 | 60 | 61·5 | 61 | 56 |

The slow variation of $\Delta$ with the temperature shows the law $\chi(T+62) = $ const. holds for this substance between about 140° K. and 290° K., the reason being obvious from the separation of $E_1$, $E_2$ and $E_3$ given above. Below 140° K. $E_2$ is only partially excited while between 140° and 290° K. the population of $E_1$ and $E_2$ will hardly vary and $E_3$ is not appreciably excited until a temperature of about 700° K. is reached.

The calculations bring out clearly the fact that $\Delta$ is only approximately constant over a limited range of temperature and has no definite physical significance. It is therefore more appropriate to exhibit the effect of the crystalline field by giving the variation of $\mu_{eff}$ with the temperature.

The early calculations of Penney and Schlapp on the properties of the rare-earth sulphates were made for the case of a crystalline field of cubic symmetry and with the tacit assumption that all the paramagnetic ions in the unit cell of the crystal lattice were magnetically equivalent. As later experimental and theoretical work has shown that neither of these assumptions corresponds to reality, the results of these calculations will not be discussed. The class of rare-earth compounds most completely investigated both experimentally and theoretically is the ethyl sulphates. They are specially suitable for systematic investigation as all the rare earths give isomorphous hexagonal crystals of this kind. The arrangement of the ions in the crystal is known and the symmetry of the crystalline electric field can almost certainly be taken as $C_{3h}$ (threefold vertical axis, horizontal plane of reflexion symmetry). There are two rare-earth ions per unit cell but these two are magnetically equivalent so that the ethyl sulphates are the theoretically simplest case of paramagnetic crystals of non-cubic symmetry. One susceptibility parallel and one perpendicular to the symmetry axis is sufficient to characterize the magnetic properties of these crystals.

Elliott and Stevens, assuming a crystalline field of symmetry $C_{3h}$ for all the rare-earth ethyl sulphates, have calculated the energy levels and their hyperfine structure due to coupling between the electronic magnetic moments and the magnetic moment and the electrical quadrupole moment of the nucleus. The problem was to find the values of the constants involved which would give a satisfactory reproduction of the experimental data on crystal susceptibility, specific heat and, above all, paramagnetic resonance (p. 145) for these salts.

The potential of the crystalline field of symmetry $C_{3h}$ can be written as

$$V = A_2^0(3z^2 - r^2) + A_4^0(35z^4 - 30r^2 z^2 + 3r^4)$$
$$+ A_6^0(231z^6 - 315r^2 z^4 + 105r^4 z^2 - 5r^6)$$
$$+ A_6^6(x^6 - 15x^4 y^2 + 15x^2 y^4 - y^6)$$

where the $A$'s are constants to be determined by comparison with experiment. The results of the calculations for some of the rare-earth ions with an odd number of electrons (Kramers, degeneracy) are given in Table 15.

In the cerium salt the ground state should be split into three doubly degenerate levels. Resonance experiments have indicated the presence of two low lying levels with $g_\parallel = 0.955$, $g_\perp = 2.185$ and $g_\parallel = 3.72$, $g_\perp = 0.20$ respectively in the cerium salt diluted with the corresponding diamagnetic lanthanum salt. In the diluted salt the first of these levels is the ground level, the other level being situated about 3 cm.$^{-1}$ higher but in the undiluted salt the order is reversed.

Susceptibility measurements on cerium ethyl sulphate crystals in the helium temperature range show that the crystals are magnetically very anisotropic and indicate the presence of two doubly degenerate levels with $g_\parallel = 3.80$, $g_\perp = 0.20$ for the lower and $g_\parallel = 1.0$, $g_\perp = 2.25$ for the upper level, the separation being about 5.2 cm.$^{-1}$. Measurements of $\chi_\parallel - \chi_\perp$ from 14–300° K. agree well with values extrapolated from the above-mentioned observations of $\chi_\parallel$ and $\chi_\perp$. The specific heat of the cerium salt has also been measured and shows a Schottky effect corresponding to the presence of two doubly degenerate levels with a separation of $4 \cdot 6$ cm.$^{-1}$. There is thus good agreement with the theoretical predictions.

TABLE 15

| Ion | Ce$^{+++}$ | Nd$^{+++}$ | Sm$^{+++}$ | Dy$^{+++}$ |
|---|---|---|---|---|
| $A_2^0\overline{r^2}$ | $-15$ | $-15$ | $0$ | $0$ |
| $A_4^0\overline{r^4}$ | $-40$ | $-35$ | $-30$ | $-40$ |
| $A_6^0\overline{r^6}$ | $-92$ | $-60$ | $-54$ | $-30$ |
| $A_6^6\overline{r^6}$ | $1150$ | $640$ | $590$ | $330$ |
| $g_\parallel$ theor. | $0 \cdot 955; 3 \cdot 72$ | $3 \cdot 56$ | $0 \cdot 64$ | $10 \cdot 3$ |
| $g_\perp$ | $2 \cdot 185; 0 \cdot 22$ | $2 \cdot 12$ | $0 \cdot 63$ | $0$ |
| $g_\parallel$ expt. | $0 \cdot 955; 3 \cdot 72$ | $3 \cdot 535$ | $0 \cdot 596$ | $11 \cdot 3$ |
| $g_\perp$ | $2 \cdot 185; 0 \cdot 20$ | $2 \cdot 073$ | $0 \cdot 604$ | $0$ |

The ground state of the neodymium ion should split into five doubly degenerate levels, with positions given below, if the crystalline field constants given in Table 15 are employed for the calculation.

| Energy (cm.$^{-1}$) | $g_\parallel$ | $g_\perp$ |
|---|---|---|
| 0 | 3·56 | 2·12 |
| 130 | 0·73 | 3·64 |
| 170 | 2·73 | 0 |
| 340 | 2·34 | 2·03 |
| 350 | 1·62 | 0 |

Resonance observations have found a doubly degenerate level with $g_\parallel = 3 \cdot 535$, $g_\perp = 2 \cdot 073$. Measurements of $\chi_\parallel$ and $X_\perp$ have shown that both susceptibilities obey Curie's law up to about 100° K. and indicate the presence of a doubly degenerate level with $g_{\shortparallel} = 3.54$, $g_{\perp} = 2.08$. Above 100° K. another level is being populated, possibly four levels between 100° K. and 300° K. Calculations of $\chi_{\shortparallel}$ and $\chi_{\perp}$ for the five levels given in the table above agree quite well with the experimental observations over the whole temperature range 1–300° K. So again there is good agreement between theory and experimental data.

For the samarium salt resonance observations indicate the presence of a doubly degenerate level with $g_{\shortparallel} = 0.596$, $g_{\perp} = 0.604$. Susceptibility measurements in the helium temperature range indicate a level with $g_{\shortparallel} = 0.615$, $g_{\perp} = 0.625$, a second level with $g_{\shortparallel} \simeq 1$, $g_{\perp} = 0$ being populated between 4° K. and 20° K., and a third level with $g_{\shortparallel} \simeq 0.8$ at about 70° K.

These rare-earth salts give absorption spectra with sharp lines at low temperatures corresponding to transitions between the various low lying levels. In the case of the samarium salt lines have been observed corresponding to two levels at 55 cm.$^{-1}$ and 65 cm.$^{-1}$. The crystalline field constants in Table 15 lead to levels at 0, 10, 60 cm.$^{-1}$. Resonance experiments have shown that there appear to be two kinds of crystal with presumably slightly different crystalline fields. A mixture of the two types would explain the observed susceptibilities.

Susceptibility measurements on the dysprosium salt indicate a doubly degenerate ground state with $g_{\shortparallel} = 11.3$, $g_{\perp} = 0$ and a higher level for which $g_{\perp}$ is not zero. Resonance experiments would not detect this ground state and the observed signal corresponds to an excited state 15 cm.$^{-1}$ higher with $g_{\shortparallel} = 5.86$ and $g_{\perp} = 8.4$. Ytterbium ethyl sulphate is interesting as being the last of the rare-earth salts, having one positive hole in the $4f$ shell. Cooke *et al.* have shown that in the liquid helium temperature range $\chi_{\shortparallel}$ follows Curie's law but $\chi_{\perp}$ is independent of temperature. The crystal is thus very anisotropic, particularly at lowest temperatures. The ground state was found to have $g_{\shortparallel} = 3.40$ and $g_{\perp} = 0$ in agreement with the theoretical predictions. No paramagnetic resonance has been observed in this salt and no resonance would be expected for a ground state with $g_{\perp} = 0$.

For the rare-earth ions with an even number of electrons the situation is quite different. In a crystalline field of symmetry $C_{3h}$ the ground state should be split into one non-degenerate level (singlet) and $J$ doubly degenerate levels (doublets). A theorem by Jahn and

Teller indicates that in such a case the crystalline field will be distorted to a lower symmetry and the remaining degeneracy of the levels removed. For the undistorted $C_{3h}$ symmetry $g_\perp = 0$ for each doublet and so no resonance should be obtained for any of the transitions. However, resonances have been observed with the ethyl sulphates of praseodymium, terbium, and holmium which all belong to this type of ion. The broad asymmetric absorption lines observed can be accounted for by a crystalline field of the type postulated by Elliott and Stevens with reasonable values of the various constants provided there is also a random distortion of Gaussian type present in the salts of the even number ions. The theory is more complicated than that for the odd number ions and no attempt will be made to summarize it here.

In addition to the effects of the crystalline field the paramagnetic ions are subject to dipole–dipole interactions between the atomic magnetic moments and to exchange interactions. In the case of salts with such a large molecule as the ethyl sulphates and particularly so in the case of salts diluted with an isomorphous diamagnetic diluent, the splittings due to these interactions are very small ($0.01$ cm.$^{-1}$ or less). They are therefore of no significance for susceptibilities at $1°$ K. or higher but are important at the temperatures obtained by adiabatic demagnetization and lead to the transformation from paramagnetism to anti-ferromagnetism at temperatures of the order of $0.01°$ K.

The paramagnetic phenomena shown by the ions of the first transition group (Ti to Ni) differ considerably from those of the rare-earth ions. In this group the $3d$ shell is incomplete, being gradually built up from one $3d$ electron in Ti to seven $3d$ electrons in Ni. In the ions the incomplete group of electrons is the outermost group and furthermore, the multiplet intervals of these ions are much smaller than in the rare-earth group. Consequently the splitting of the various levels by the crystalline field are now of the same order of magnitude as the multiplet intervals and the calculations of the susceptibility is greatly affected. Van Vleck has shown that the effect of the crystalline field in such a case is to uncouple the $L$ and $S$ vectors and partially or completely 'quench' the $L$ moment. The magneton number then lies between that given by writing $S$ for $J$ in (10), i.e. spin moment only and that obtained from

$$\chi = Ng^2\beta^2\{S(S+1)+L(L+1)\}/3kT$$

i.e. $L$ and $S$ effective but uncoupled from one another, in agreement with the experimental values.

In the cyanides such as potassium ferricyanide in which the bonding is covalent rather than ionic, the effect of the crystalline field is still more drastic. Not only the $L.S$ coupling but also the $s.s$ coupling is broken down so that the spins pair off as far as possible and the observed magnetic moment corresponds approximately to $S = \frac{1}{2}$, instead of $S = \frac{5}{2}$, as in ferric ammonium alum.

Paramagnetism is also observed in those elements in which there is a buildup of the $4d$ (Mo, Ru, Pd), the $5d$ (Re, Ir, Pt) and the $5f$ ($6d$) (the transuranic elements). Many interesting problems have still to be solved with the compounds of these elements.

## Paramagnetic Resonance

When a solid paramagnetic is placed in a magnetic field the remaining degeneracy of the paramagnetic ions is lifted and a set of Zeeman energy levels produced. The allowed transitions are those for which the change of magnetic quantum number $= \pm 1$. If now a small alternating magnetic field of frequency $\nu$ is applied perpendicular to the main magnetic field, allowed transitions are induced between the Zeeman levels when the quantum of energy $h\nu$ is equal to the energy separation of adjacent levels, and energy is absorbed by the spin system from the alternating magnetic field. Thus an absorption line is observed when the resonance condition $h\nu = g_{ik}\beta H$ is satisfied ($g_{ik}$ is a factor similar to the Lande splitting factor of the free ion but is a tensor for a paramagnetic crystal). From the number and position of the observed absorption lines it is possible to obtain the value of $g_{ik}$ as a function of direction in the crystal and the number and position of the lowest zero-field energy levels of the ions. If the nucleus of the paramagnetic ion possesses a magnetic moment and/or an electric quadrupole moment, the absorption lines may show a hyperfine structure from which these nuclear moments can be derived. The paramagnetic resonance method also shows immediately whether there are two or more non-equivalent ions in the unit cell of the crystal and gives information about the crystalline field around each such ion. If the resolution is adequate the contribution to the hyperfine structure from each isotope of the paramagnetic ion can also be found. Again the presence of impurities is not important as the absorption lines due

10

to the main constituent and the impurities can in general be readily identified. The method is thus a much more powerful one than measurement of susceptibility where the interpretation in terms of the sum total of the contributions due to all populated levels is at best difficult and sometimes impossible. The resonance method, however, only gives information regarding the ground state and any low lying excited states (a few cm.$^{-1}$ above the ground level) which are sufficiently populated at the low temperature of the observations. Resonances may not be observed for several reasons. States with $g_{\perp} = 0$ give no resonances and the relaxation time of various states may be too short and so the line width of any transitions too large in spite of lowering the temperature and diluting the paramagnetic salt.

For atomic moments and a magnetic field of a few thousand oersteds the resonance frequency falls within the microwave range (wavelength $0\cdot1$–5 cm.). It is experimentally more convenient to work at constant frequency and adjust the main magnetic field to satisfy the resonance condition. This field is then modulated at low frequency so that it sweeps through the resonant value and the signal due to the absorption is exhibited on a C.R. tube.

The paramagnetic resonance technique has added very greatly to our knowledge of the state of ions in paramagnetic crystals. Some of the data on the rare-earth ethyl sulphates collected by this method have already been mentioned in the discussion of the crystalline field theory.

## Paramagnetic Saturation

When the ions in a crystalline solid can be considered as free and are all in the same energy state, the magnetization per gram ion is given by

$$\sigma = Ng\beta \frac{\sum\limits_{M=-J}^{M=+J} M e^{-[(Mg\beta H)/(kT)]}}{\sum e^{-[(Mg\beta H)/(kT)]}} \tag{12}$$

in which $M$ takes successively the values $J(J-1),\ldots -(J-1), -J$, corresponding to the possible orientations of the magnetic moment with respect to the direction of the magnetic field. Equation (12) can be transformed into

$$\sigma = NJg\beta B\left(\frac{Jg\beta N}{kT}\right) \tag{13}$$

with
$$B(x) = \frac{2J+1}{2J} \coth\left(\frac{2Jx+x}{2J}\right) - \frac{1}{2J} \coth\left(\frac{x}{2J}\right)$$

This Brillouin function may be compared with the classical Langevin formula

$$\sigma = N\mu\left[\coth\left(\frac{\mu H}{kT}\right) - \frac{kT}{\mu H}\right]$$

Equation (13) has been plotted in Fig. 32 for the case $J = \frac{7}{2}$, together with the classical formula with the same slope at the origin and thus the same $\mu_{\text{eff}}$. For small values of $\mu_{\text{eff}}H/kT$, equation (13) gives a

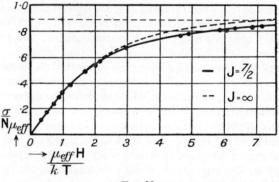

FIG. 32

linear relation between $\sigma$ and $H/T$ (Curie's law, $\chi$ independent of $H$) and reduces to expression (10). For larger values of $\mu_{\text{eff}}H/kT$ the magnetization is no longer proportional to $H$ but tends more and more to a 'saturation' value when the ionic magnetic moments are completely aligned by the magnetic field. At room temperature the value of $\mu_{\text{eff}}H/kT$ is so small even with the strongest magnetic fields obtainable that the magnetization lies on the initial straight part of the curve, and to observe the approach to saturation it is necessary to extend the measurements to very low temperatures. Woltjer and Kamerlingh Onnes determined the magnetization of gadolinium sulphate, at temperatures down to $1\cdot31°$ K. and in magnetic fields up to 22 kilo-oersted. The experimental points, some of which are plotted in Fig. 32, fit well on the curve of expression (13) with $J = \frac{7}{2}$ as required by the $^{8}S_{7/2}$ ground state. At the highest field strength and lowest temperature used the observed magnetization reached about 95 per cent of that which would be produced by the complete alignment of the ionic magnetic moments.

Gorter, de Haas and van der Handel later investigated potassium chromium alum down to $1·34°$ K. and in fields up to 19 kilo-oersted. From the behaviour of this substance at higher temperatures, where it obeys Curie's law accurately, it must be concluded that the magnetic moment of the $Cr^{+++}$ ion is due entirely to the spin moment ($S = \frac{3}{2}$), the $L$ moment being completely suppressed by the crystalline field. In agreement with this the observed magnetizations lie on the curve of expression (13) when $J$ is taken as $\frac{3}{2}$. The observations have more recently been extended by Henry to $1·29°$ K. and 50 kilo-oersted, the highest observed magnetization corresponding to $99·5$ per cent saturation.

An examination of the quantum theory curve and the classical one discloses a characteristic difference between the two theories. For a given value of $\mu_{\text{eff}}$, defined as on p. 130 and derived from observations at higher temperatures, the quantum theory gives a saturation moment of $NJg\beta = N\{J/(J+1)\}^{1/2}\mu_{\text{eff}}$, while the classical theory gives $N\mu_{\text{eff}}$. Thus in Fig. 32 the asymptote of the classical curve is at $\sigma/N\mu_{\text{eff}} = 1$, whereas that of the quantum curve is at $(\frac{7}{9})^{1/2} = 0·88$, the horizontal dotted line. The explanation of the difference lies in the fact that according to the quantum mechanics, the angular momentum of an atom is given by $\{J(J+1)\}^{1/2}h/2\pi$ and that in a magnetic field the atom precesses round the direction of the field so that the component of the angular momentum along the field is

$$\{J, J-1, \ldots -(J-1), -J\}h/2\pi$$

Thus at saturation the total angular momentum makes an angle of $\cos^{-1}\{J^2/J(J+1)\}^{1/2}$ with the field, whereas in the classical case the magnetic moment is exactly aligned along the field when the substance is saturated.

### Magnetic Rotation of the Plane of Polarization

When plane polarized light is passed through a transparent substance placed in a longitudinal magnetic field the plane of polarization is rotated. With diamagnetic substances the rotation is proportional to the applied magnetic field and independent of the temperature: with paramagnetic substances it is of the opposite sign, proportional to the field and inversely proportional to the absolute temperature at the higher temperatures. It thus appears that the rotation is proportional to the magnetization of the substance and that therefore it should show saturation phenomena at sufficiently low temperatures in the case of paramagnetic solids. This has been shown to be the case by Becquerel and de Haas. They measured the rotation of single crystals of various minerals such as tysonite (a complex fluoride of Ce, La, Nd and Pr) and of certain pure salts such as dysprosium ethyl sulphate in fields up to 30 kilo-oersted and at temperatures down to $1\cdot3°$ K. The phenomena shown by the dysprosium salt are the simplest observed and most readily interpretable; only these will be discussed.

The theory of the paramagnetic rotation of the plane of polarization has been developed by Kramers on the basis of his calculations of the effect of the crystalline field on the energy states of paramagnetic ions in solids. He showed that if the temperature is so low that all the ions are in the lowest sub-level into which the ground state of the free ion is split in the crystal the rotation is given by

$$\omega = a\tanh\left(\frac{\mu H}{kT}\right) + bH \tag{14}$$

in which $\mu$ is the effective magnetic moment of the ion in the direction concerned, $a$ and $b$ are constants and the second term is small compared with the first. The curve of $\omega$ as a function of $H/T$ is thus similar to that of Fig. 32 and the rotation shows a definite saturation for high values of $H/T$.

The observations of Becquerel and de Haas on dysprosium ethyl sulphate at $4\cdot21°$ K. and $1\cdot62°$ K. for the case in which the direction of the magnetic field and that of propagation of the light are coincident with the principal axis of the hexagonal crystal can be accurately represented by Kramers' formula with an effective magnetic moment of $5\cdot66\beta$ in excellent agreement with the value ($5\cdot67\beta$) derived from susceptibility measurements at these temperatures. It is, furthermore, the only case in which practically complete saturation has been observed, the curve at 27 kilo-oersted and $1\cdot62°$ K. being lower than the asymptote by less than 1 part in 100,000.

Since the ground state of the dysprosium ion $^6H_{15/2}$ is split into eight doubly degenerate sub-levels by the crystalline field the simple formula (14) will no longer hold when the temperature is high enough for the separation between the sub-levels and $kT$ to be comparable, because then the higher sub-levels will also contribute to the rotation. This proves to be the case for the observations at $20.35°$ K.; since $kT$ at $20.35°$ K. is about 14 cm.$^{-1}$ the separation between the ground state and the next higher sub-level of the dysprosium ion must be less than or at most comparable with this value, in agreement with the estimate from resonance observations (p. 143).

The magnetic rotation of the plane of polarization by crystals at very low temperatures thus enables one to observe the phenomenon of paramagnetic saturation more readily than the rather laborious susceptibility measurements and, as Becquerel has shown, the susceptibility of the crystal parallel to the optical axis can be derived directly from the optical measurements.

## Antiferromagnetism

In Heisenberg's interpretation of the Weiss molecular field of ferromagnetics the calculation of the energy of the ferromagnetic involves an exchange integral. When this integral is positive the lowest energy state is obtained when all the atomic moments are parallel. The substance then shows spontaneous magnetization and the various other ferromagnetic properties. If, on the other hand, the exchange integral is negative there should be a corresponding tendency for the atomic moments to be oriented alternately in opposite directions so that, if all the atomic moments are identical, the local magnetization is zero at saturation. It is believed that the phenomenon shown by various oxides and fluorides of the transition elements and known as antiferromagnetism can be explained on this basis. These substances are paramagnetic at the higher temperatures but below a certain temperature usually referred to as the Néel point, the susceptibility diminishes rapidly with fall in temperature. At this temperature the antiferromagnetics exhibit an anomaly of the cooperative type in the specific heat.

Antiferromagnetic behaviour has also been observed in single crystals of $CuCl_2 . 2H_2O$, $T_N$ (Néel point) = about $5°$ K., and of $CoSO_4 . (NH_4)_2SO_4 . 6H_2O$, $T_N = 0.084°$ K. It is also found in the iron and chromium alums below the lower of the two specific heat maxima and in certain of the rare-earth metals.

The theory of antiferromagnetism has been developed by Néel and by van Vleck on the assumption that the atomic magnetic moments are situated on two interpenetrating space lattices with antiferromagnetic interactions between them. The Weiss molecular field theory is then used to calculate the magnetic behaviour of the system. Thus the molecular field of lattice $A (= H_A)$ and that of lattice $B (= H_B)$ can be written as

$$H_A = H - \alpha M_A - \beta M_B$$
$$H_B = H - \beta M_A - \alpha M_B$$

in which $H =$ external magnetic field, $M_A$, $M_B$ magnetization of lattices $A$ and $B$, $\alpha$ and $\beta$ positive Weiss constants. Above the Néel point this leads to an expression for the susceptibility $\chi(T + \theta) = C$, with $\theta = C(\alpha + \beta)/2$, of the form of the Curie-Weiss law which generally holds for paramagnetics. This law holds for these substances down to $T_N$ which is seen to be equal to $C(\beta - \alpha)/2$. Below $T_N$ the susceptibility is found to diminish rapidly. The ratio $\theta/T_N = (\beta + \alpha)/(\beta - \alpha)$ is found to vary from about 1·4 to 5. For MnO, the first antiferromagnetic to be recognized as such, $\theta = 610°$ K., $T_N = 122°$ K.

The presence of the two sub-lattices with antiparallel orientation of the atomic magnetic moments below the Néel point has been established for MnO and other antiferromagnetics by neutron diffraction studies. The spin of the neutron interacts with the atomic moments and so the neutron is differently diffracted by the two lattices. Thus below the Néel point 'extra' lines appear in the diffraction pattern but disappear above this temperature in the same way as extra lines appear in the X-ray diffraction patterns in ordered alloys and disappear when the structure becomes disordered at some higher temperature.

### Nuclear Alignment

In the discussion of the method by which temperatures of the order of $10^{-5°}$ K. have been obtained, it was mentioned that a magnetic field of about 100,000 oe. can produce a large degree of alignment of the nuclear magnetic moments at a temperature of, say, 0·01° K. Such a system of oriented nuclei provides the nuclear physicist with a very valuable opportunity of studying the angular variation of various nuclear processes, beta and gamma ray emission, neutron scattering, etc. This has become a very fertile field of investigation and has opened up a new chapter in physics involving the close collaboration of nuclear and low temperature physicists.

There are a number of methods by which an alignment of the nuclear moments can be achieved. First of all the direct method mentioned above and frequently referred to as the 'brute force' method in which a high magnetic field is combined with a very low temperature. Unfortunately the requirements for both factors are almost at the limit of what can be obtained at present. For a proton a magnetic field of 50,000 oe. and a temperature of $0.02°$ K. will result in a 20 per cent polarization of the nuclear moments.

Gorter and also Rose pointed out that the electrons in an atom produce a magnetic field of some $10^5$–$10^6$ oe. at the nucleus and that at $0.01°$ K. the nuclear moments will be largely aligned by this field. There is an interaction between the nuclear spins and the atomic moment which leads to the hyperfine structure of spectral lines. Thus if the atomic moments are aligned by an external magnetic field the nuclear moments will also be aligned through the h.f.s. interaction. The advantage of the method is that a field of a few hundred oersteds is adequate to align the atomic moments at temperatures of the order of $0.01°$ K.

Again Bleaney drew attention to the fact that at sufficiently low temperatures the atomic moments in a single crystal are aligned with respect to the axis of the crystalline electric field even in the absence of any external magnetic field. The nuclear moments will then be aligned by the h.f.s. interaction along these same crystallographic directions.

The mechanism for the alignment of the atomic moments may also be ferromagnetic or antiferromagnetic interaction and again through the h.f.s. interaction the nuclear moments will be aligned along the direction of the domain magnetization.

Nuclear alignment can also be produced by employing the interaction of the crystalline electric field gradient with the nuclear electric quadrupole moment (Pound).

While the direct method and the Gorter-Rose method produce nuclear polarization, the Bleaney and Pound methods result only in nuclear alignment as parallel and antiparallel orientations with respect to the preferred axis are equally present.

In using the direct method the sample has been cooled indirectly by means of demagnetized iron ammonium alum in which were embedded a number of silver wires to the outer ends of which the sample was attached.

To apply the Gorter-Rose and Bleaney methods a small amount of the ion whose nuclear properties are to be studied, is introduced into the lattice of a suitable paramagnetic salt to form a mixed crystal. The amount of the ion added is determined by a compromise; sufficient to give a reasonable experimental accuracy and not so much that excessive heating of the lattice by the radioactive process occurs.

Thus $Co^{59}$ and $Co^{60}$ have been introduced into the mixed Tutton salt $(Co, Cu, Zn)SO_4 . Rb_2SO_4 . 6H_2O$ with one per cent Co, 12 per cent Cu, 87 per cent Zn. The disadvantage of the Tutton salts is that they contain two non-equivalent paramagnetic ions per unit cell and so there are two axes of the crystalline field along which nuclear alignment takes place. Nickel fluosilicate for which there is only one such axis is more suitable and is used for the divalent ions of the first transition group.

The trivalent ions of the rare earths may be introduced into cerium ethyl sulphate or cerium magnesium nitrate. The latter has a particular advantage for the Gorter-Rose method. It is extremely anisotropic magnetically and if a magnetic field is applied perpendicular to the axis of the crystal and then removed the lattice will cool. A field sufficient for the alignment of the atomic moments can then be applied parallel to the axis without causing any appreciable rise in temperature.

Nuclear alignment has been used to study the anisotropy of the emission of $\alpha$, $\beta$ and $\gamma$ rays and the absorption of polarized neutrons. From the observations the spin of the nuclear states involved in the transitions can be determined and the nature (magnetic or electric dipolar or quadrupolar radiation) of the emission of the $\gamma$ rays. A considerable amount of data has already been collected for an account of which the reader is referred to the Bibliography, p. 156.

The most striking result so far of this collaboration between low temperature and nuclear physics is the test by Ambler and Hudson and their co-workers of the Lee-Yang theory of the non-conservation of parity in certain nuclear processes. It was predicted that non-conservation should be observable in the $\beta$-ray emission from aligned nuclei. This was verified.

# Bibliography

**Chapter I**

*Encyclopedia of Physics* (*Handbuch der Physik*), vols. 14 and 15, Springer, Berlin, 1956.

M. Ruhemann, *Separation of Gases*, 2nd ed., Oxford University Press (1949).

R. B. Scott, *Cryogenic Engineering*, Van Nostrand Co. Inc., New York (1959).

G. K. White, *Experimental Techniques in Low-Temperature Physics*, Oxford University Press (1959).

F. E. Hoare, L. C. Jackson and N. Kurti, *Experimental Cryophysics*, Butterworths, London (1961).

C. G. Garrett, *Magnetic Cooling*, John Wiley & Sons Inc., New York (1954).

**Chapter II**

*Temperature, Its Measurement and Control in Science and Industry*, vols. 1 and 2, Reinhold Publishing Corp., New York (1941, 1955).

**Chapter III**

W. H. Keesom, *Helium*, Elsevier, Amsterdam (1942).

F. London, *Superfluids*, vol. 2, John Wiley & Sons Inc., New York (1954).

K. R. Atkins, *Liquid Helium*, Cambridge University Press (1959).

L. D. Landau and E. M. Lifshitz, *Statistical Physics*, chap. 6, Addison-Wesley Publishing Co. Inc., Reading, Mass., U.S.A. (1958).

C. G. Gorter, *Progress in Low Temperature Physics*, vols. 1 and 2, articles on liquid and solid $He^4$ and $He^3$, North-Holland Publishing, Amsterdam (1955, 1957).

J. Wilks, 'Theories of Liquid Helium II', *Reports on Progress in Physics*, vol. 20 (1957).

V. P. Peshkov and K. N. Zinov'eva, 'Experimental work with $He^3$', *Reports on Progress in Physics*, vol. 22 (1959).

A. A. Abrikosov and G. M. Khalatnikov, 'The Theory of a Fermi Liquid', *Reports on Progress in Physics*, vol. 22 (1959).

## Chapter IV

M. Blackman, 'Theory of the Specific Heat of Solids', *Reports on Progress in Physics*, vol. 8 (1942).

W. K. Parkinson, 'Specific Heat of Metals', *Reports on Progress in Physics*, vol. 21 (1958).

C. Kittel, *Solid State Physics*, 2nd ed., John Wiley & Sons Inc., New York (1957).

## Chapter V

N. F. Mott and H. Jones, *The Theory of the Properties of Metals*, Oxford University Press (1936).

A. H. Wilson, *The Theory of Metals*, 2nd ed., Cambridge University Press (1953).

D. A. Wright, *Semiconductors*, 2nd ed., Methuen's Monographs on Physical Subjects, London (1955).

D. Shoenberg, *Superconductivity*, 2nd ed., Cambridge University Press (1952).

F. London, *Superfluids*, vol. 1, John Wiley & Sons Inc., New York (1950).

C. Kittel, *Solid State Physics*, 2nd ed., John Wiley & Sons Inc., New York (1957).

## Chapter VI

J. H. van Vleck, *Electric and Magnetic Susceptibilities*, Oxford University Press (1932).

E. E. Stoner, *Magnetism and Matter*, Methuen & Co. Ltd. (1934).

L. F. Bates, *Modern Magnetism*, 3rd ed., Cambridge University Press (1951).

C. G. B. Garrett, *Magnetic Cooling*, John Wiley & Sons Inc., New York (1954).

B. Bleaney and K. W. H. Stevens, 'Paramagnetic Resonance', *Reports on Progress in Physics*, vol. 16 (1953).

K. D. Bowers and J. Owen, 'Paramagnetic Resonance, II', *Reports on Progress in Physics*, vol. 18 (1955).

D. Shoenberg, 'The de Haas-van Alphen Effect', *Progress in Low Temperature Physics*, vol. 2 (1957).

# Index